HAWAI'I'S Spa
EXPERIENCE
Rejuvenating Secrets of the Islands

Hawai'i's Spa Experience

Rejuvenating Secrets of the Islands

Sherrie Strausfogel and
Sophia V. Schweitzer

MUTUAL PUBLISHING

All rights reserved
Library of Congress Catalog Card
Number: 2004111146

First Printing, October 2004
1 2 3 4 5 6 7 8 9

Design by Sachi Kuwahara Goodwin

ISBN 1-56647-687-9

Mutual Publishing, LLC
1215 Center Street, Suite 210
Honolulu, Hawai'i 96816
Ph: 808-732-1709 / Fax: 808-734-4094
email: mutual@mutualpublishing.com
www.mutualpublishing.com

Printed in Korea

This book

is dedicated

to all the

healers,

therapists, and

estheticians

throughout

our Islands

who bless with

their touch.

Small, heated lava stones, as used here at The Spa at the Four Seasons Resort Maui, gently deepen the pressure of a soothing massage. (Photo courtesy of The Spa at the Four Seasons Resort Maui)

Contents

"Mahalo nui loa" to all who gave kind assistance and gracious hospitality
in the research and production of this book.

Mahalo to the spa directors, public relations directors, and sales and marketing directors:
Peter Georgeson and Alan Ogomori for Abhasa Waikīkī Spa, Robin Desha for Ihilani Spa, Judy
Hollister for Mandara Spa, Will Shimabukuro for Na Ho'ola Spa, Joyce Matsumoto and Tony Young
for SpaHalekulani, Paul Brown and Peter Shin for Spa Olakina *Salon, Vivienne Gan and Eric Kwan
for Spa Suites, Nancie Brown for Spa Grande, Bea Wolfe for Spa Hotel Hāna-Maui, C. J. Arquette and
Liz Marquez for Spa Kea Lani, Leah Chin for Spa Moana, Lori and Jim Kennedy
for The Spa at Four Seasons Maui, Shelby Taylor for Waihua—A Place of Wellness, Donna Kimura
for Hualālai Sports Club & Spa, Pat Eli for Kohala Sports Club & Spa, Crystal Poe-Cabatbat
for Mauna Lani Spa, Jessica Ferracane for Spa Without Walls and Robin Jumper for ANARA Spa
Mahalo for your spa wisdom:
Sylvia Sepielli of Sylvia Planning and Design, who created SpaHalekulani and Mauna Lani Spa;
Sharon Warren of Warren Botanicals; and Emma Wright of E'SPA
Mahalo for travel arrangements:
Hawaiian Airlines and David McNeil and Sandi Yara of McNeil Wilson Communications

And a heartfelt mahalo to Les Enderton for "importing" me to Hawai'i,
for always being the first to read my words, and for trying that first facial.
— Sherrie Strausfogel

To write about the healing aspects of the Islands is a privilege. I am grateful to have had the
opportunity to explore the sybaritic side of such work. Thank you to all the spa directors who
patiently explained treatments, showed facilities, and graciously invited me to experience their spas.
Thank you to the many public relations directors who went out of their way to accommodate me
during Hawai'i's busy spring-break season. Thank you to Claire Morris-Dobie at the Hyatt Regency
Kaua'i, Shelby Taylor at the Ritz Carlton, Kapalua, and Bea Wolfe and Doug Chang at Hotel
Hāna-Maui for your generous hospitality. A special thank you to Sharon Warren for your unwavering
energy in developing recipes and, above all, your inspirational love for the power of plants.
— Sophia V. Schweitzer

Clear pools, smooth rocks, and sparkling waterfalls: Hawai'i is a place to heal. (Photo by Sri Maiava Rusden Photography)

Sweet pineapples were introduced to the Islands in 1813. (Photo by Douglas Peebles)

Island keiki (children). (Photo by Sri Maiava Rusden Photography)

A chaos of rainbows lit by dancing rays of sun... (Photo by Douglas Peebles)

UNIQUELY HAWAIIAN: A BLEND OF CULTURES

About 1,800 years ago, a small group of men and women set out from the southern Marquesas in double-hulled canoes. Guided solely by the pattern of waves and winds and the flight of birds, they navigated the vast Pacific Ocean for more than a thousand miles. Aboard, they carried about twenty-four plants that would provide food, rope, clothing, and medicine once they found land—healing noni and refreshing coconut among them.

They found the verdant, deep-clefted valleys and buoyant rivers of the Hawaiian Islands' windward sides, and did not hesitate to settle. A chaos of rainbows lit by dancing rays of sun touched down on the valley floors. There was snow on at least one mountain, despite the comfortable warmth near the shores. Not far away, freshwater springs brought life to the parched soil of the islands' leeward sides. Tranquil bays and clear ocean waters lent themselves to the creation of fishponds. The trade winds caressed the voyagers' sunburned skin. And here were thousands of unfamiliar plants, ready to be picked and used.

Whatever caused these early Hawaiians to undertake their arduous journey, they had found a place to rest and heal. They farmed and gathered from ocean, river, and land. Their diet was simple—the taro root that they had brought was their staple—and so healthy that in the Hawaiian language the word for indigestion did not exist.

Hawai'i's white sand beaches. (Photo by Sri Maiava Rusden Photography)

A bountiful land of fertile valleys and warm shorelines. (Photo by Douglas Peebles)

Taro root was the staff of life for the Hawaiian people. It is still grown in many places. (Photo by Douglas Peebles)

Of course, there was a need for medicine. The two-dozen plants they had brought in their voyaging canoes—which we now collectively refer to as "canoe plants"—were familiar. Hawai'i's native plants, however, had evolved in total isolation, seeded in young volcanic soil. Most of them did not exist anywhere else in the world. They discovered the healing powers of these new plants through sharp observation.

A unique health care system developed, centered on deep respect and reverence for this bountiful new homeland. It had to embrace the unavoidable and frightening reality of active volcanoes, tsunamis, floods, and droughts—phenomena that they believed the gods controlled and that were intimately connected to one's physical, emotional, and spiritual health. The Hawaiian people came to understand that all things were interconnected. Each plant, each person, each animal, and even each natural disaster or blessing had its purpose. This was the concept of *lōkahi*, the interdependence and unity of all life.

So much has changed since those early days, and yet, the old ways have survived. Directly and indirectly, bound to a natural environment, they define what modern Hawai'i is about.

In 1779, Captain James Cook put Hawai'i on the maps and charts. From that time, for-
eigners with different ways of healing made Hawai'i their home. In the latter half of the
nineteenth century, large sugar plantations, rather than ancient taro patches, gradually
came to dominate the landscape. Immigrant laborers from Asia arrived by the thousands.
Encountering the difficult demands of plantation life, they were grateful that they had
brought their own medicines, and relied on their own healing traditions to stay well.

And so, after a day of carrying sheaves of sugar cane on his back, the Chinese bache-
lor massaged his neck and shoulders. He pressed hard on points that would regenerate the
life force he knew as *qi*. To remain calm and balanced under the cries of the *luna*, the over-
seer, he practiced the gentle martial art of *tai chi*. The Japanese drank tea in sacred ceremonies filled with symbolism and mindfulness. They soaked away their aches and sorrows
in the baths that they called *furo*. And the Filipino laborers in later years brought herbs that
would burn with sweet healing smoke, as well as other medicinal foods. Western sailors,
merchants, missionaries, and plantation owners came with their own fruits, plants, and
ways of keeping healthy: citrus fruits, mineral baths, chocolate, coffee. A few decades later,

*Vanilla, the bean of
an exotic orchid, has
infused soothing oils
since ancient times.
(Photo by Ray
Wong)*

*Japanese drank tea
for ceremonies and
pleasure. (Photo
courtesy of
Mandara Spa)*

*Coffee first came to
the Islands via King
Kamehameha's
personal physician.
(Photo by Douglas
Peebles)*

wealthy travelers from Europe and America began to arrive at Honolulu's Aloha Tower on spectacular cruise liners. They named the Pali Lookout, at the top of the precipitous pass over O'ahu's Ko'olau Mountains, "the most beautiful view in the world" in 1933—and brought with them all the luxurious comforts of the opulent European spa.

Eventually, the dreams and traditions that came with Western and Asian immigrants blended with the ways of old. The fragrance of plumeria and jasmine, the lavender veil of the blossoming jacaranda trees, and the exuberant colors of wild orchids—all brought in by the newcomers—have made Hawai'i even more exotic than it was in ancient times.

Founded by Hawai'i's royalty, Honolulu has grown into an international hub of glamorous shops, high-tech architecture, world-class dining, and cosmopolitan flair. And in recent decades, international luxury resorts have sprung up along Hawai'i's sun-splashed beaches, often situated on ancient healing sites. As is the trend in travel these days, they feature splendid, modern spas. Against a backdrop of palm trees and beaches, these oases of rejuvenation welcome the men and women eager to leave behind the bustle of cities, daily business, noise, and chronic stress.

Ko'olau Mountains, one of Hawai'i's dramatic mountain ranges. (Photo by Douglas Peebles)

The coconut was once the Hawaiian's most versatile plant. (Photo by Ray Wong)

The spa in Hawai'i is unlike other spas. Its menu reads like poetry in motion, visiting east and west, picking up fragrances and techniques along the way, and coming to rest in the Islands. The spa reflects Hawai'i's cultural melting pot. It adds another layer to the healing traditions that have been gathered here throughout the centuries. It is not only about ancient Hawaiian healing—and yet without the Hawaiian traditions, the spa in Hawai'i could not be what it is.

The spas cherish the diversity of Hawai'i's healing techniques and ingredients. Visionaries like Papa Henry Auwae (1906–2001), one of the most noted Hawaiian healers in modern times, say that a renewed interest in Hawaiian culture—ancient hula, the Hawaiian language, Hawaiian *mele* (song)—and a deepening western appreciation of ethnic healing modalities have opened a pathway to harmonize old and new. The interdependence and unity of all life, understood so well by the Hawaiians, find parallels in what is today known as mind-body medicine—an essential element of the spa.

Spa treatments in the Islands do their best to integrate traditional views on healing and celebrate the Islands' unique history. Almost all offer Hawaiian *lomilomi* massage. In

The exuberant fragrances and colors of exotic flowers augment Hawai'i's tropical ambiance. (Photo by Ray Wong)

People have applied cooling, rejuvenating mud to their skin for centuries. This photo shows a mud treatment at the Mauna Lani Spa. (Photo courtesy of Mauna Lani Resort, Big Island)

treatments, they may incorporate native plants, lava rock, and rituals inspired by old Hawaiian ways, or they may simply emphasize the healing gifts of the Islands—the sound of lapping waves and gentle winds. They might use products grown on Hawaiian soil—sugar, coffee, or macadamia nuts, to name a few. Many spas incorporate the best of East and West: high-tech European techniques such as Swiss showers or hydrotherapy, or Asian elements such as Thai massage and acupressure. All Hawaiian spas keep up with contemporary trends, opening fitness centers, creating special treatments such as vigorous massages and thorough facials for men, and linking health to spirituality and mindfulness.

This book will guide you to the spas and spa ingredients of Hawai'i—both products of the Islands. Throughout these pages, you will learn more about Hawaiian healing methods as well as Asian traditions and current thoughts about the modern spa.

You will also find details on how to create the spa experience at home through treatment recipes with easy-to-find ingredients, soothing foods and teas, and island-style ways to relax.

Handy references and addresses are at the end of the book.

Keep in mind that spas are always evolving, and that spa signature treatments may change over time. Be discerning as you experiment. With your bare feet on the sand, with the touch of *aloha*—that singular Hawaiian word that means breath, caring, and love—take a few hours to relax.

We hope that this book helps you discover your own Hawaiian healing ways. The saying goes: *Ola Mai Iloko Mai*—Health comes from within.

A note of caution: this book is not intended to serve as medical advice. Some treatments, especially those that involve heat, should not be chosen under certain medical conditions, including pregnancy and heart disease. Consult your doctor if you have any doubts.

Ocean view from Hyatt Regency Kaua'i Resort & Spa. (Photo courtesy of ANARA Spa and Hyatt Regency Kaua'i Resort & Spa)

Coconut, mango, and oats: healing ingredients from Hawai'i's multicultural traditions. (Photo courtesy of Hyatt Regency Kaua'i Resort & Spa)

Smooth, heated rocks were used in massages in ancient Hawaiian times. (Photo courtesy of Hilton Waikoloa Village)

Bromeliads—among them health-giving pineapples—thrive in Hawaiian soil. (Photo by Douglas Peebles)

A detoxifying mud masque is made of a clean, pure, and clay-based substance. (Photo by Sri Maiava Rusden Photography)

Historic illustration.
(Courtesy of
Four Seasons Resort
Hualālai)

PRODUCTS FROM HAWAIIAN SOIL

Recently, renewed respect for older traditions has resulted in a spectrum of spa products that incorporate all things natural and botanical. Native medicine believes in the powers of nature— and the fact is, the healing plants of ethnic cultures truly do contain powerful bioactive chemicals. The curative compounds in hundreds of pharmaceuticals find their origins in humble plants—periwinkle to fight cancer, digitalis for the heart, and papaya to digest protein.

In Hawai'i, endemic and indigenous plants—those that grew here before the first voyagers came—were supplemented by Polynesian species. At least four of these natives—'awa, wild ginger, *noni*, and mountain apple—have garnered the medical community's interest. A handful have found their way to the spa.

Long after the Polynesian arrivals, new plants came with each group of immigrants to Hawai'i's shores. They thrived, for the Hawaiian Islands are blessed with a subtropical climate and fertile volcanic soils. The presence of high mountains and tradewinds conspire to bless each island with a windward side of abundant rain and flowing rivers. Majestic tree ferns, native 'ōhi'a, macadamia nut orchards, avocado trees, and strawberry fields flourish side by side.

As a result, a new economy of diversified agriculture blossoms on fallow plantation fields, in large part to supply Hawai'i's healthy, fresh, and ethnically-inspired regional cuisine.

Soft, sweet, sensual, and often Asian, these locally grown ingredients—modern and old—are equally essential to the Hawaiian spa.

'Awa
'Alaea
'Awapuh (Ginger)

ENDEMIC, INDIGENOUS, AND POLYNESIAN INGREDIENTS

In traditional Hawaiian medicine, herbal lore was part of a much larger and more complex tradition of healing. The *kahuna laʻau lapaʻau*—the expert in healing herbs—worked in a team with other *kahuna* who had other specialties: perhaps massage, prayer and chanting, pregnancy or childbirth. Healing required self-awareness, an honest look at one's relationships, and a sincere realignment with the gods. Papa Henry Auwae was fond of saying that 80 percent of the healing process was spiritual, and the rest came from plants and herbs, and other products of the earth. Here are just a few of these ingredients, adopted—and adapted—by the spas.

ʻALAEA

Found in veins deep within the most weathered mountains of the islands, this water-soluble, rust-red clay added soothing salve to Hawaiian medicine, counteracting the biting sting of *paʻakai* (sea salt), with which it invariably was mixed. Fatty, rich in minerals, mixed with essential oils, the iron-oxide found in *ʻalaea* is said to cleanse and nourish. Today's spas use it in Hawaiian sea-salt body scrubs that exfoliate, tighten, and soften skin.

ʻAWA (KAVA)

The heart-shaped leaves of this member of the pepper family grace Hawaiʻi's shady valley floors. The gnarled roots made for a bitter, astringent beverage, kava, which made farmers nod off without body aches and sent chiefs and priests into a trance. Nicknamed "a massage from the inside out," this canoe plant is still used in many South Pacific cultures to relieve anxiety and stress. In the spas, it is used in soothing body wraps.

ʻAWAPUHI (GINGER)

Surrounding waterfall pools in damp forests, the red, torch-shaped blossoms of wild ginger, *ʻawapuhi kuahiwi*, introduced by ancient Polynesians, froth with a soapy liquid when squeezed—a most natural shampoo. Its spicy roots are similar to Asian *ʻawapuhi ʻai*, edible ginger, with its fiery potential to improve circulation, digestion, and many ailments of the skin. Ginger's essential oil relieves nausea, congestion, and muscle pains. The intensely fragranced, delicate-flowered white ginger, *ʻawapuhi keʻokeʻo*, is a most popular flower in Hawaiian leis, as well as in products of the Island's spas.

ʻIliahi (Sandalwood)

The sweet, balsamic perfume from this evergreen's wood infused Hawaiʻi's forests for hundreds of years. Calming and cooling, it was used to scent layers of *kapa* cloth. In the 1800s, a sandalwood trade sprang up to supply China with the fragrant, prized wood, which had grown so rare in Asia that it was at times more precious than gold. Sandalwood powder and essential oil uplift the spirit and center the heart.

Kī (Ti)

Seen near shady river beds and at the four corners of local houses—it is said to bring good fortune and chase off evil spirits—the sweet-starchy root of this canoe plant made for a fiery bootleg liquor in the nineteenth century. The majestic, glossy leaves are said to soothe fevers, headaches, and other body aches. Spas apply them in cooling body wraps.

Kō (Sugar Cane)

Once a treat for Hawaiʻi's royalty and a gentle sweetener for bitter medicine, the graceful, noded stalks of sugar cane, with their plumage of rustling leaves, gave rise to Hawaiʻi's all-transforming sugar industry. Spa treatments may use Hawaiian turbinado sugar made from cane's first pressing, with the fragrance of molasses. Mixed with aromatic oils, its moist, grainy texture gently exfoliates and protects the skin. Sugar is also said to have antiseptic properties.

Kukui (Candlenut Tree)

This silvery-leaved member of the Spurge family glimmers in forests across the islands, and was one of the Hawaiians' most valued plants. Today it is Hawaiʻi's state tree—its delicate flowers and shiny nuts still are used for leis—but it once yielded medicine, *kapa* dye, and balm for ailments of the skin. Its oily, laxative nuts were strengthening. They served as candles and provided fuel for torches and lamps. Emollient, clear, and rich in fatty acids, the oil protects skin and hair. Essential oils mixed with it quickly penetrate the skin.

Limu (Sea Plants)

Whether they are apple-green wisps, translucent voile, amber-colored parchment, or crisp, dark-rose clumps along Hawaiʻi's lava-strewn coasts, these nutrient-packed sea plants and algae are integral to the modern spa. Once used for ocean-related ritual and medicine, from canoe blessings to the healing of coral cuts, different varieties are now mixed with essential oils and used for skin-nourishing wraps and scrubs.

'Iliahi (Sandalwood)

Kī (Ti)

Kō (Sugar Cane)

*Kukui
(Candlenut Tree)*

Limu (Sea Plants)

MAILE

Found on mountainous slopes around the islands, this native, twining shrub was and is a favorite ceremonial plant of the Hawaiian people, used for decorations and leis. Said to represent in its four variations four hula deities, *maile* is intimately connected to the goddess Laka and the hula dance. Its vine-like leaves, when crushed, release a grounding, calming scent reminiscent of earth and vanilla.

NIU (COCONUT)

Seen in clusters high up in slender palm trees that grow close to the shore, the coconut was once the Hawaiian's most versatile plant, providing anything from thatching to drink and medicine. Its sweet meat yields a creamy, emollient oil with a clean scent, which, conditions hair and skin, and when heated, eases muscle aches. Grated, the pulp adds texture and sultry fragrance to spa body scrubs.

NONI (INDIAN MULBERRY)

Often found fermenting in the sun in large glass jars in local gardens, the pale yellow, warty fruit of this glossy-leaved tree yields a clear, strong-tasting juice. Locals swear by its revitalizing magic; it is said to nourish the blood. Researchers are studying its potential in pharmaceuticals. Traditionally this canoe plant was said to heal urinary trouble, boils, fractures, and cuts. It is also an effective sunburn soother.

'ŌLENA (TURMERIC)

The vivid saffron hues in the knobby rhizomes of this botanical relation of the ginger family lend their pigment to the robes of Buddhist monks in Asia, and to the patterns of ancient Hawaiian *kapa* cloth. Pungent, spicy, even peppery, it is said to purify the blood and, in Hawaiian medicine, makes for a sinus decongestant. On many islands in the Pacific, turmeric is thought to ward off evil spirits and is worn as a protective charm. The spas love its vibrant

Maile
Niu (Coconut)
Noni (Indian Mulberry)

qualities for beautiful, purifying body scrubs. It is said to have skin-healing properties.

Botanicals from the First Decades after Contact

With European merchants, Asian plantation laborers, and missionaries from America's eastern seaboard, hundreds of new plants arrived in the Islands. From Asia came fragrant flowers and exotic fruits—white ginger, orchids, and jasmine; mango, starfruit, and lychee. Western sailors brought the citrus fruits that prevented scurvy among their crews, as well as root stock that might deliver tradable goods. The missionaries brought with them pretty ornamentals, to remind them of home. These plants from the four corners of the globe have all found their way into contemporary island life, gracing gardens, tables—and luxurious spa treatments that take advantage of their healing and nourishing properties.

Pānini ʻAwaʻawa (Aloe)

Grown on back porches and near kitchens around the world, this spiky-leafed succulent was readily adopted by the Hawaiians for its cooling power. The clear gel that oozes out when the leaf tip is broken off brings instant relief to minor burns and scratches. In lotions and body wraps, aloe soothes sunburn and moisturizes dry skin.

Coffee

Rustling with sheer sheets of white blossoms or laden with red, plump cherries, Hawaiʻi's coffee trees dot Kona's volcanic slopes as well as other island orchards, where afternoon clouds prevail. First introduced by King Kamehameha's personal physician, planted as an ornamental in Kona by Samuel Ruggles, a devout missionary, coffee has become the state's stimulant. The aromatic, ground roast, when mixed with essential oils, makes for delicious body scrubs.

ʻŌlena (Turmeric)
Aloe (Pānini ʻAwaʻawa)
Coffee

MACADAMIA NUT

Found in abundance in the large orchards that border the rain forests of Mauna Loa, this plump, crunchy Australian nut wasn't brought to the Islands until 1882. Buttery and smooth, it has become so ubiquitous that the Big Island is known as the macadamia nut capital of the world. It is a favorite with island chefs, and the spas love its clear, unctuous oil for the way it lingers to soften and nourish skin and imparts a glow to sun-damaged hair.

PĪKAKE (JASMINE)

With small, intensely fragrant flowers that resemble delicate roses, *pīkake* originates from India, where it is associated with the god of love. It owes its Hawaiian name to Princess Ka'iulani, the heiress to the Hawaiian throne who is said to have died of a broken heart after the overthrow of the monarchy in 1893. She filled her gardens both with jasmine and with colorful, free-roaming peacocks, and the little white flower from the Indian subcontinent became known as the peacock flower, *pīkake*. *Pīkake* lifts the mood and burdened mind, and reduces fatigue and stress. It induces healing and peaceful rest.

ORCHID

With more than 12,000 species, and belonging to one of the largest families of flowering plants, orchids thrive in the diverse climate zones of subtropical Hawai'i. They are known more for their exquisite, complex and long-lasting beauty than for their scent, but one species, *Orchis morio*, has purple, green-veined flowers and a mild, enticing fragrance. The blossom yields an extract—oil of orchid—said to have exceptional skin softening, moisturizing, and soothing properties. This rare product enhances select spa formulas.

ROSE

Sweet, ethereal, complex, and romantic, rose is probably the one scent and aromatherapy oil that no spa can do without. Indeed, rose oil is used in 96 percent of women's perfumes, and it contains hundreds of bioactive compounds that work together in harmony. Rose, it is said, is good for the skin and the soul. It is a tonic for the mind. Rose lifts the spirit, alleviates tension and stress, calms, and even acts as a gentle aphrodisiac. Cleansing, toning the blood, and possessing antiseptic qualities, rose stimulates life energies—*mana* in the Hawaiian language. The Islands are home to a native rose, *lokelani*, which has no thorns.

Macadamia Nut
Pīkake (Jasmine)
Orchid
Rose

Vanilla
Lavender
Papaya
Pineapple

Modern Products of the Islands

Although papaya, vanilla, avocado, and pineapple are found in other tropical regions, it is the rich presence of all these fruits and flowers, native plants and introduced species together that makes Hawai'i the special place it is. These relative latecomers are now part of Hawai'i's abundance. They augment the flavors of every-day local life. Rich, bold, invariably healthy and delightful to the senses, they have also found a niche in the Island's spas.

Vanilla

The vanilla bean is actually the seed of an orchid plant occasionally found in abandoned Japanese-Hawaiian gardens. The fragrant cured vanilla bean has spurred a cottage industry in Hawai'i in recent years that requires Zen-like concentration: to obtain beans, each delicate flower must be pollinated by hand, preferably with chopsticks. Its sweet, seductive-but-innocent scent—said to be reminiscent of mother's milk—calms the body, relieves anxiety, soothes emotions, and relaxes the mind.

Lavender

One of the most popular relaxing herbs since ancient times, lavender yields bluish-purple flowers along slender sprigs that are a tonic for the nervous system. It has graced the graveled slopes of Mediterranean Europe with its subtle perfume since ancient times. Several farms in the uplands of Maui have recently begun to raise and harvest this cooling and faintly bitter flower. Lavender eases nervous exhaustion and tension headaches. It relieves anxiety, calms the mind, and stimulates circulation. A gargle with a concentrated infusion is said to sweeten the breath. The scent of lavender essential oil encourages deep, healing sleep.

Papaya

Hawai'i's premier export crop, the Solo papaya, traveled from Jamaica nearly a century ago. Long known to aid digestion, the tender-fleshed fruit has made an appearance on breakfast tables throughout the Islands for decades. Now the papaya, packed with enzymes and alpha-hydroxy acids, has been gratefully adopted by spas around the world to exfoliate, soften, and nourish the skin. The papaya's vivid orange color reveals the presence of carotenoids and other potent phytochemicals that slow down the effects of age.

Pineapple

Kamehameha's personal physician introduced the tangy, sweet-fruited bromeliad in 1813. A century later, plantations on O'ahu, Maui, and Lāna'i contributed to a prolific canning industry. The presence of an enzyme known as bromelain aids digestion and encourages healing. Still thriving in sunny gardens and farms, the juicy, acidic fruit with its fresh, tropical scent cleanses, smoothes, and softens the skin.

Maile leaves release a calming scent when crushed. (Photo by Ray Wong)

An outdoor massage brings the sound of lapping waves. (Photo courtesy of Ihilani Spa)

Let yourself be pampered, here at the Spa Suites. (Photo Courtesy of Kāhala Mandarin Oriental, Hawai'i)

Play and run with a smile, island-style... (Photo by Sri Maiava Rusden Photography)

HAWAI'I'S ELITE SPAS

Many of the most prized spas are situated in the Edenic places, where in ancient times the ali'i (kings and chiefs) played or convalesced. They inhabit the sunny spots that cradle golden beaches and sapphire-studded ocean waves, with luxury resorts that reawaken romance and lift pampering to the level of art. The addresses of more luxury resort spas can be found at the end of the book.

Yoga on the grounds of Kāhala Mandarin Oriental. (Photo courtesy of Kāhala Mandarin Oriental, Hawai'i)

O'ahu

The most populous of the Hawaiian Islands, O'ahu still harbors a plethora of serene places. The windy North Shore, famous for its winter waves, the windward plains around Kailua and its long sugar-sand beach, and Central O'ahu with its orchards and farmlands, all calm the spirit in different ways. On the leeward side, secluded from the quickened pulse of Honolulu, beaches, lagoons, and coves bejewel the rural western plains at the foot of the Wai'anae Mountains.

As for spas, the resort community of Ko'Olina sparkles in calm isolation along O'ahu's south-western tip. On the east side of Diamond Head, exclusive, quiet Kāhala hugs a crescent of golden beach and is home to an intimate boutique spa. But most of O'ahu's healing treatments can be found near Diamond Head's western side, in world-renowned Waikīkī.

Long before beach front hotels and high-end shops replaced taro patches and duck ponds, Hawai'i's royalty resided in Waikīkī when seeking to rest and relax. Once a marsh nourished by three streams, Waikīkī—"the place of spouting water"—became a focal point for healing traditions that developed around its freshwater channels, its warm ocean water, cool sea breezes, and languid air.

Today, millions of people come to the shores of Waikīkī each year to play and, perchance, to heal. Here, bordered by a calm canal on one side and the ocean on the other, spas nestle against each other along Kalākaua Avenue. Escape within their sanctuaries—with the latest healing traditions—and you will quickly leave the crowd behind.

In ancient Hawai'i, the feet were considered precious. SpaHalekulani starts each treatment with a grounding foot ritual. (Photo courtesy of SpaHalekulani)

Spa facility at the Abhasa Waikīkī Spa at The Royal Hawaiian Hotel. (Photo courtesy of Abhasa Waikīkī Spa)

Abhasa's body cocoon turns a herbal wrap into a nurturing experience. (Photo courtesy of Abhasa Waikīkī Spa)

Abhasa Waikīkī Spa

Built on a former marshland of native grasses and ponds, this oasis within an oasis at the Royal Hawaiian Hotel sits in the shade of a giant monkeypod tree, adjacent to a tropical garden where finches trill among canna lilies and plumeria trees. Such a place of respite is hard to find in the heart of this modern metropolis. Indeed, Abhasa is the only spa here to offer outdoor cabana massages—on a small, secluded garden patio.

To add sensuality and a tropical touch to your choice of massage, Abhasa offers a selection of aromatherapy oils created in the Islands. The ginger and jasmine blend is warming, romantic, and relaxing, reminiscent of tropical nights. Lavender, geranium, and tangerine are said to bring serenity. A revitalizing blend of lemongrass, grapefruit, lavender, and peppermint refreshes and invigorates.

Abhasa is one of Waikīkī's first spas in one of O'ahu's oldest hotels—the "Pink Palace of the Pacific" was built in 1927—but the spa's mystique reveals itself in its rather unexpected offerings, blends of high-tech and traditional approaches.

One of the Balinese-inspired massage rooms is equipped to provide cold-laser facials that cleanse, lift, and tighten the skin. With this noninvasive treatment, your face relaxes under the cooling, soothing gel that the therapist applies before gently caressing your face with a laser wand. Enthusiasts see improved collagen production and less sun-induced pigmentation. This mild facial treatment starts and ends with a delight of essential oils to cleanse and moisturize—among them citrus to refresh and stimulate, or rose petals to relax and calm.

Equally innovative are Abhasa's enveloping cocoons that turn your herbal wrap into a healing, nurturing experience. Once the wrap is applied— and you are covered with cleansing coconut milk and soothing aloe—your massage table inflates to become a waterbed that snuggles around your body.

Abhasa also offers a powerful water massage: 240 air jets and seventy water jets massage and lift you while you soak in a fragrant mineral bath. This invigorating therapy is said to be the ideal preparation for other treatments. It relaxes tight muscles and alleviates pain.

The spa hosts an extensive salon, and guests of The Royal Hawaiian Hotel can use the fitness center at the Sheraton Waikīkī.

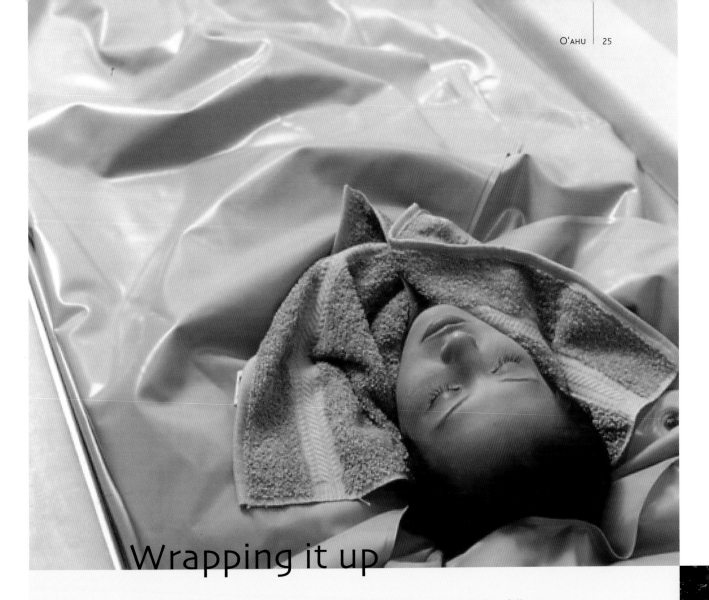

Wrapping it up

Said to prolong the healing power of plants or nurturing oils, and often following a massage, a wrap cocoons your herb-, seaweed-, or clay-balmed body in warm, damp, linen sheets and cotton towels for about twenty minutes. Sometimes a thermal blanket augments insulation. The heat and steam enhance absorption of medicinal ingredients. A long, soothing shower follows the wrap. Wraps can leave the skin soft, nourished, glowing, and radiant, relax tight muscles, and ease body aches.

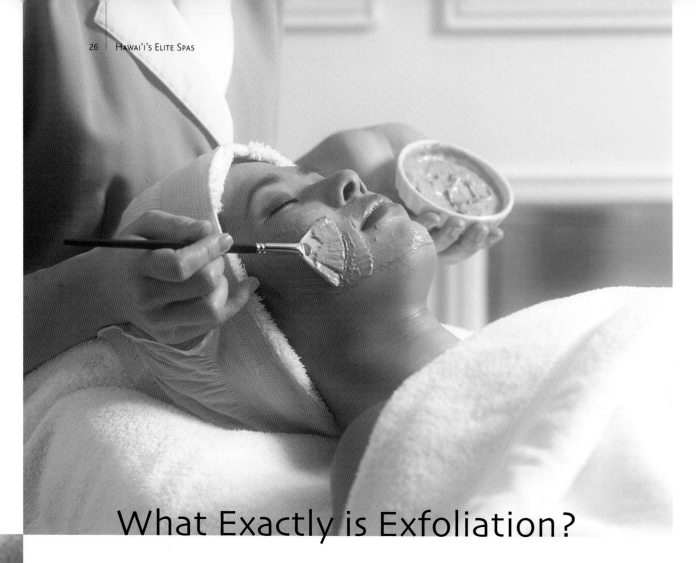

What Exactly is Exfoliation?

The skin regenerates itself rapidly. Over time, skin cells die off and are replaced.

Bathing removes old skin cells to a degree. You can facilitate the process: techniques that specialize in sloughing off dead cells are said to *exfoliate*. Leaving the skin silky soft, with new and healthy cells, they include texture-based polishes and scrubs that rely on gritty ingredients such as salt, sugar, ground nuts, or cornmeal. Alpha-hydroxy acids, found in papayas, for example, exfoliate with gentle fruit acids.

Spa treatments finish with fragrant moisturizers.

IHILANI SPA

In ancient times a fishing area prized for its salt-water lagoons, the grounds of Ko 'Olina at the foot of the Wai'anae mountains are home to a rapidly growing resort community that draws affluent travelers in search of relaxation with all the casual comforts of home. Here, Ihilani Spa at the JW Marriott Ihilani Resort and Spa at Ko 'Olina was the first spa destination to open on O'ahu, and has remained loyal to its own themes.

Ihilani pays tribute to the traditional, old-world spa with a large space dedicated to hydrotherapy—water-enhanced relaxation and water-based therapies. An oversized whirlpool spa, dry sauna and steam

Facial treatment at the Ihilani Spa. (Photo courtesy of JW Marriott Ihilani Resort and Spa at Ko 'Olina)

Roman bath at the Ihilani Spa. (Photo courtesy of JW Marriott Ihilani Resort and Spa at Ko 'Olina)

Color Light Therapy

In Ihilani Spa's thalasso-tub, you can choose to relax with color light therapy, said to balance body, mind, and spirit. Several other spas in the islands merge the healing powers of color and water.

Color has been used since ancient times to restore energy, calm emotions, lift depression, or invigorate thoughts. This is because colors have specific frequencies said to influence the frequencies of the body. A room in soothing blue or green has a different effect on our mood than a room with rousing red and orange tones.

In traditional Eastern medicine, seven different colors are said to correspond to seven different energy centers in the body, the *chakras*. In color light therapy, rays of these seven colors illuminate the water while you bathe. You can choose a rainbow of colors for overall balancing, or just one or two colors for specific healing purposes.

RED *revitalizes and builds confidence. It boosts energy and fights fatigue.*
ORANGE *symbolizes joy, releases shyness, and increases spontaneity.*
YELLOW *stimulates the mind and leads to greater wisdom.*
GREEN *restores harmony, generates love, and eases tension.*
BLUE *soothes, and brings calm and peace.*
INDIGO *awakens the intuition, and deepens perceptions.*
VIOLET *purifies, hones spiritual awareness, and allows for inspiration and creativity.*

room are surrounded by floor-to-ceiling glass walls, artful mosaics, marble, palm trees, and colorful bromeliads. The wet area includes a Swiss shower with vertically positioned rows of rotating jets as well as a Vichy shower with shower heads that align over your reposing body: the ideal rinse after scrubs.

Ihilani Spa's pride is its thalassotherapy—the ancient Greek art of creating wellness and health through the use of mineral-rich seawater and sea-plants. Its thalasso-tub, one of just two in the United States, fills with warm, fresh, filtered ocean water, straight from the lagoons. Aromatherapy oils can be added. Dozens of rotating underwater jets effective-ly soothe aching muscles and boost the circulation.

Ihilani Spa opts for the basics: it does what it does best, does it well, and uses the best of ingredi-ents. The Deluxe Botanical Body Polish starts with a sea-salt exfoliation. Oil of the *pīkake* flower—which is said to relieve depression, to stimulate creativity, and calm the nerves—is blended with the salt. The scrub is followed by a cleansing, polishing pineapple body wash. Finally, lotion scented with white orchids softens, moisturizes, and soothes silken skin.

Pua Kai, Flower by the Sea, is Ihilani's signature scent, with hints of calming rose, sensuous jasmine,

ethereal orange blossoms, spicy ginger, and exotic coconut. It is said to express the romantic spirit of the little *naupaka* flower that with its curious unfin-ished semicircle shape graces Ihilani's shores. In a tragic-sweet Hawaiian legend, it symbolizes the sep-aration of two lovers and their eternal love.

Ihilani Spa features a fitness center, tennis courts, and a Pilates room. It has fitness consultants, personal trainers, and a nutritional expert on board, and even offers hula classes. Yoga classes are offered on the ocean front lawn. Grassy knolls and reef path-ways hug the peaceful lagoons, offering serene places to meditate.

Thalasso treatment at the Ihilani Spa. (Photo courtesy of JW Marriott Ihilani Resort and Spa)

Massage at the Ihilani Spa. (Photo courtesy of JW Marriott Ihilani Resort and Spa)

*Massage at the
Mandara Spa.
(Photo courtesy of
Hilton Hawaiian
Village Beach
Resort & Spa)*

MANDARA SPA

On the edge of the Hilton Hawaiian Village Beach Resort & Spa's twenty-two acres, on the property where surf legend Duke Kahanamoku grew up, the Balinese-themed Mandara Spa embodies soothing warmth, wholeness, and serenity. On its own dedicated floor, it is rich with damask rose colors and Balinese artwork, and gentle music wafts through the air.

Mandara's couples' rooms feature private, outside whirlpool spas, ideal for soaking together after a massage. In fact, one of Mandara's fun-inspired treatments, Exploration in Chocolate, is an edible (dare we say intimate?) affair. After an unscented oil massage in tandem, you and your sweetheart are invited to dip into a chocolate, sugar, and macadamia nut scrub and rub each other with the sweet scrub: the tub is hot, music plays, tea is ready.

Mandara's signatures, however, are the treatments that use the spa's own line of aromatherapy oils. You can choose from four blends. Mandara (with sandalwood, patchouli, and ylang ylang) whispers romance, appeals to men, and is said to soothe, heal, and nourish the skin. Harmony (with lavender, bergamot, mandarin, and ylang ylang) calms, balances, and refreshes. Calming Tranquility blends vetiver and

lavender. Island Spice, with cloves, ginger, cinnamon, and lemongrass has the scent of tropical dreams. It stimulates, warms, and gives you energy.

These oils fully blossom in the Mandara Massage, a euphoric experience with four hands working in synergy, soothing body and mind with a blend of the world's greatest healing arts—including Swedish, *lomilomi*, Shiatsu, and Thai.

Among other aromatherapy treatments, you can relax with geranium, revive with lime, ease muscle pains with warming thyme and rosemary, detoxify with seaweed, juniper, and lemon, or opt for a silky facial.

Mandara's relaxation lounge located one floor below the spa—a secluded lānai with bamboo, ferns and other water-loving plants—features a whirlpool spa, a rain shower, a steam room, and a sauna with aromatic sandalwood, said to uplift and center the spirit. It is adjacent to a fitness center, a spa cuisine café, and a quiet swimming pool.

Treatment room at the Mandara Spa. (Photo courtesy of Hilton Hawaiian Village Beach Resort & Spa)

Aromatherapy

Have you ever squeezed an orange rind to enjoy the revitalizing scented oil that bursts forth? Since ancient times men and women have used fragrant plant oils in religious rites, in perfumes, and in the healing arts. Today, the therapeutic use of essential oils—natural, high-quality, and pure extracts distilled from plants, leaves, bark, roots, seeds, resin, and flowers—is called aromatherapy.

The volatile, odoriferous molecules of these essential oils affect the brain and our sense of well-being when inhaled. Tiny amounts of a scent can trigger memories and emotions. They are easily absorbed by the skin and are said to have medicinal properties.

Aromatherapy alleviates stress. The oils relax, stimulate, harmonize, refresh, and rejuvenate. Lavender is calming. Rosemary eases muscle pains and invigorates. Peppermint energizes. Hundreds of essential oils exist, of which aromatherapists and spas regularly use about forty in their precise and balancing blends of oils.

One of the most popular and effective aromatherapy products used in Hawai'i spas is the Relief Line (see Appendix). Numerous massages finish with a few drops of awakening, refreshing eucalyptus-infused respiratory relief oil or start with a stress-relieving oil.

NA HO'OLA SPA

In the heart of Waikīkī overlooking the peaceful Pacific, the four sacred stones of Kapaemahu whisper of magical times and *kahuna* healers. It is said that these *pōhaku* were the farewell gifts of four Tahitian priests, who in the 1300s brought health and well-being to the Hawaiian people. Na Ho'ola Spa, on the fifth and sixth floors of the Hyatt Regency Waikīkī Resort & Spa, gazes from floor-to-ceiling windows down upon these stones, and its name—"Many Healers"—refers both to the ancient traditions and the healers the spa employs today.

Na Ho'ola, indeed, maintains an intimate connection to Hawaiian healing and culture; its symbol is four Hawaiian healing plants. Most in demand is Hawaiian *lomilomi* massage, given only by therapists who have been trained by traditional teachers. Styles and practitioners may vary, but what makes *lomilomi* so powerful is that it always begins with a *pule* (prayer)—often silent—and requires an open heart and loving hands.

Among signature treatments is the Na Ho'ola Body Polish, which is gentler to the skin than a sea-salt scrub. Ground grapeseed—packed with antioxidants and mixed with refreshing aloe—gives a fine, gritty texture to a scrub base of silky macadamia nut and grapeseed oils. After the polish, a papaya-pineapple and kukui nut oil moisturizer completes the exfoliation and leaves the skin cleansed and soft.

For its Na Ho'ola Deluxe Facial, the spa offers a choice of a mild and scrumptious organic line with a cleansing, uplifting red rose masque that sings of wild European gardens in the height of summer or a pumpkin-orange masque that hydrates the skin while whispering of the comfort and warmth of fall. Or choose from a more assertive treatment based on a stimulating peel with hot cinnamon, or a gentle, mineral-rich masque with sea plants and ocean minerals for sensitive skin. Before and after pictures taken with a high-resolution camera reveals skin that is visiably clearer and smoother.

Na Ho'ola Spa offers yoga classes and has a small, sunny fitness room.

Treatment room at the Mandara Spa. (Photo courtesy of Hilton Hawaiian Village Beach Resort & Spa)

View from Na Ho'ola Spa. (Photo courtesy of Hyatt Regency Waikīkī Resort & Spa)

Lomilomi Massage

Almost every spa in Hawai'i offers *lomilomi*, the world-famous massage that originated here in the islands. When practiced within the spirit of Hawaiian healing and culture, it transcends mere technique to become a true healing experience.

In a *lomilomi* massage, the therapist uses long, gliding, rhythmic movements that ease tension, relax muscles, and stimulate the blood flow and lymphatic system. The pressure—often applied with elbow or forearm as well as hands—may be invigorating and strong.

Lomilomi can precede or incorporate a *pōhaku* massage; in a *pōhaku* treatment, the therapist uses heated lava stones either with gentle pressure with certain massage strokes (which intensifies the effect) or simply by placing them on energy-points along the spine, hands, and feet.

In the Hawaiian language, the word *lomilomi* means simply "to rub, to press." True *lomilomi*, however, goes beyond the sensuous, feel-good touch. It is part of a healing ceremony that seeks to realign a person in body, mind, and soul. Healing, in Hawaiian medicine, has all to do with setting things right. Hawaiian healers see physical problems as mere reflections of imbalances within one's own conscience, with loved ones, or the natural environment.

Lomilomi is about an inner faith and attitude. The *lomilomi* practitioner must feel a heart-to-heart connection to the person in his or her care. Whether spoken out loud or not, the practitioner includes prayer, *pule*, to ask for guidance and protection, and to express gratitude and humility. Chant may be included as well.

For centuries, the ancient knowledge of *lomilomi* stayed within a family, and was passed down from generation to generation. It took decades to understand, and included knowledge of herbal medicine and balancing meditation techniques.

Auntie Margaret Machado—known by anyone involved in the healing arts in Hawai'i—may well have been the first *kahuna lomilomi* to share the secrets of the practice with the outside world. She loves to say that *lomilomi*, essentially, is "the art of love and healing through the hands and heart."

Lomilomi has a sacred, cleansing purpose. In ancient days, it prepared warriors mentally for battle, and eased their physical pains. Hula dancers received *lomilomi* before performances, chiefs before important decisions had to be made. Today, as much as then, it is still the giving, loving spirit of *lomilomi* that opens the heart and allows the *mana*, the life energies, to flow.

In lomilomi, the pressure applied with the elbow or forearm eases tension and invigorates. (Photo courtesy of Mandara Spa)

Small pōhaku, lava stones, are often placed on energy points along the spine, hands, and feet. (Photo courtesy of Hilton Waikoloa Village)

View of the pool at Halekulani. (Photo courtesy of Halekulani)

SpaHalekulani

Just east of today's Halekulani on the beach at Waikīkī a freshwater channel from natural springs runs through the reef and is known as the cleansing water of Kawehewehe, "the opening up." Here, the ancient Hawaiians bathed to find wellness, and offered *limu* leis to the healing gods.

As one of the younger spas in Waikīkī—its sliding Japanese doors opened in April 2003—the much-awarded SpaHalekulani embraces all the cultures that are at the root of Hawai'i today, placing particular emphasis on those from the South Pacific. *Kapa* cloths from Tonga and Samoa, tropical grass mats, bamboo, and bleached Thai wood reflect its intimate Polynesian ambiance.

Each of its seven treatment rooms is equipped with a private steam-shower and changing room, allowing you to relax in your own private sanctuary from beginning to end of your treatment. The couples' room includes a Japanese-style *furo* bath.

To ground your healing journey, and prior to any treatment, SpaHalekulani offers a gentle foot-pounding ritual. In this welcoming touch, your feet are briefly wrapped in fragrant, steaming towels, then rhythmically tapped with silk-clad Polynesian *pū'ili*, bamboo hula rattles, and lastly misted with refreshing, cleansing Mānoa mint and tea tree oil.

Fresh *maile* leaves await you on your sandal-wood-scented massage bed. When crushed, they release a rain forest-green, citrus-light scent. Their ethereal oils are soothing yet invigorating, calming yet clear. In Hawaiian traditions, the *maile* vine is used for celebrations and special occasions. Aptly, it is SpaHalekulani's signature fragrance.

South Pacific specialty therapies at SpaHalekulani include Polynesian Nonu, a Samoan massage that uses smooth stones wrapped in mulberry bark, and toning, revitalizing *noni* juice. Signature among them is the Polynesian Steam Therapy, inspired by Tongan traditions. After a gentle, tapping-style massage to loosen the upper chest and back, this treatment envelops you in your own humidifying steam tent made of authentic *kapa* cloth. While your feet are pampered with reflexology, you inhale the lemony vapors of lemongrass, said to have antiseptic and skin-healing properties, along with earthy mists of kava root, said to ease anxiety and instill a profound calm, and eucalyptus to let you breathe easy.

No matter what experience you choose, Spa Halekulani prolongs your sense of well-being on its private patio where, after your treatment, you can dream a little longer while savoring frozen melon and sipping fragrant hibiscus tea.

Lobby of SpaHalekulani. (Photo courtesy of the Halekulani)

A Man in the Spa?

Yes, spas in Hawai'i and elsewhere cater to men. Men have their own steam room, sauna, and locker room. Spas formulate aromatherapy and other product lines with men's preferences in mind. This is simply a development—probably here to stay—in response to the thousands of men who know that a good workout, relaxing treatments, and soothing massages rejuvenate the body, soothe emotions, aid the body's natural healing capacities, and calm an overburdened mind. Hawaiian *pōhaku* (hot stone) massages and gentlemen's facials are favorites for men in island spas.

SPA OLAKINO *SALON

On the site of Queen Lili'uokalani's summer villa and her tranquil lily ponds, where she came to recuperate from the tensions and pressures of 'Iolani Palace, renowned stylist Paul Brown has opened a luxury spa with calming, natural forest-and-water elegance at the Waikīkī Beach Marriott Resort and Spa.

The Hawaiian concept of *olakino* denotes health and wellness. At Spa Olakino *Salon, sage-green tones, Balinese teaks, tropical prints, sensual sculptures, Buddha statues, trickling water fountains, and soft faux lava walls from which *hinahina* moss trails infuse the space with a peaceful Hawaiian feel. The lounge area gives tranquil views of busy Waikīkī Beach.

Spa Olakino prides itself on using natural, fresh ingredients—including exfoliating and oil-rich coffee grounds, nourishing honey, calming 'awa, invigorating and cleansing lemongrass, soothing aloe gel, and antioxidant-rich green tea—that are crushed, pounded, brewed, or mixed right on the spot. These make for plant-based recipes that (with a little creativity and a few drops of aromatherapy oil) can easily be adapted for the home spa.

Spa Olakino has not one but several shower and steam rooms. One of these is inside a tandem room, making the space ideal for couples who want to share scrubs and wraps.

The Magic Island Massage is Spa Olakino's ultimate signature massage, infused with aromatic, warming ginger, it combines the yoga-like stretches of Thai massage, Shiatsu to awaken the energy-flow, Hawaiian *lomilomi* with its meditative, strong, and loving movements, and reflexology to affect the internal organs through pressure points on the soles of the feet. The treatment invigorates, soothes, balances, and eases physical aches all at once—a great choice for men.

You may want to finish your massage with a gentle, polishing scrub made of soft-gritty cornmeal that has been blended into an enzyme-rich papaya, pineapple, and *kukui* nut base. The alpha-hydroxy acids in the papaya and pineapple enhance the grain-based exfoliation.

Another signature option is the slightly more vigorous Ke Kai, which is Hawaiian for "the sea." This scrub integrates mineral-rich sea salt and detoxifying Big Island-grown spirulina (an algae) with healing scents of calming lavender and sensual, uplifting ylang ylang.

Naturally, Spa Olakino *Salon features an extensive Paul Brown hair salon. It is also adjacent to a fitness center where yoga classes are offered.

All spas cater to men. Photo taken at Mandara Spa. (Photo courtesy of Mandara Spa)

*Masque at the Spa Olakino *Salon. (Photo courtesy of Olakino *Salon)*

Spa Suites

Just east of Diamond Head, the Kāhala Mandarin Oriental resort hugs the blue Pacific in a quiet, upscale neighborhood. Here, the sun rises over Koko Head against the splendid backdrop of the Ko'olau Mountains to the north. A tranquil garden path meanders through bamboo, hibiscus, palms, and gingers, passing smiling Buddha statues as an afterthought. The path leads to five enclosed mini-gardens that serve as the entrances to five peaceful, spacious suites with eucalyptus floors, sea-grass carpets, bright anthuriums, Balinese teaks, and Hawaiian plantation louvers that let in the breezes.

These are the resort's subdued, secluded, stylish Spa Suites. They each measure 550 square feet, and include a private bathing area with an infinity-edge jet tub, where trickling water cascades down.

Each treatment at Spa Suites begins with a brief foot-cleansing ritual. Your therapist eases your feet into a *kamani*-wood bowl filled with warm water and Hawaiian 'alaea salts. After a relaxing soak, she massages and exfoliates your feet with refreshing spearmint to energize and uplift. This is also the time to choose, from the spa's several organic aromatherapy oils, the blend that in your subsequent massage and bath will heal and please you most. The oils include soothing, uplifting neroli made from orange blossoms,

refreshing lemon, calming frankincense, cleansing eucalyptus, and awakening and purifying juniper.

Spa Suites offers creative, basic treatments—Life Saving Back Massage and Stress Reliever Aromatherapy, for example, and even more creative holistic signature treatments, Pi'ha Kino and Lōkahi.

Pi'ha Kino and Lōkahi start alike. They each ready your skin with a gentle cactus-bristle body brushing and a cooling spearmint and aloe polish that make your skin feel radiant and soft. Next, you luxuriate in an infinity-edged tub swirling with aromatherapy bath oil, detoxifying liquid seaweed, and mineral sea salt.

Pi'ha Kino follows with a gentle-yet-firm massage. To release lingering tensions, your therapist places warm basalt *pōhaku* on your hands and feet, and sometimes on the body's seven *chakra* energy-points along your spine. The treatment continues with a gentle massage around the eyes, temples, and jaws, then finishes with a calming, centering scalp massage.

Lōkahi integrates more Hawaiian healing elements with a rhythmic, dynamic *lomilomi* massage, soothing, nurturing *kukui*- and macadamia nut oils, and fresh *ti* leaves that are said to relax and cool.

The Kāhala Mandarin's Chi Fitness & Balance Center offers state-of-the-art equipment and a menu of fitness classes. To find a serene place to meditate, wander to the end of the narrow peninsula on the east side of the property, where private benches look out over lapping waves.

A mask suggesting quiet and silence at the entrance to the Spa Suites.

View of a room at the Spa Suites.

Yoga comes into its own when practiced in natural, peaceful settings. Here, on the lawn at the Kāhala Mandarin Oriental. (Photos courtesy of Kāhala Mandarin Oriental)

Yoga

At least 5,000 years old, the art of yoga originally evolved as a series of disciplines that might help practitioners reach a sense of oneness with the universe. Indeed, "yoga," a Sanskrit word, means "union." In its purest form, yoga was part of a lifestyle devoted to awakening. It involved meditation, mindfulness, and the practice of loving kindness.

In one yoga tradition, Hatha, the physical body itself became the gateway to greater awareness and harmony. *Asanas* (physical poses), and *pranayama* (controlled breathing exercises) prepared the body for the spiritual path. Even without a spiritual component, however, yoga's *asanas* provide significant physical and psychological benefits.

Today, many spas offer a variation of Hatha yoga. Yoga's stretches release both tense muscles and emotions. Active yet gentle, easily adapted to any fitness level or age group, yoga increases strength and flexibility, improves balance and posture, promotes relaxation, reduces anxiety and stress, calms and clears the mind, builds confidence, and uplifts the spirit. It is said to restore the flow of *prana*, life's vital energy.

Yoga comes into its own when practiced in natural, peaceful settings. In Hawai'i, yoga classes are often offered at sunrise and sunset, on the beach, or on an ocean-side knoll or lawn.

Maui

Maui can get busy at peak vacation times with visitors drawn to its playful, sunny-side-up allure. Yet away from the crowds, its natural splendor and serene beauty inspire peacefulness and quieter pastimes. Beyond the resort communities of Kāʻanapali and Kapalua, a hike in the West Maui Mountains might reveal eroded cliffs and deep valleys. And on the windward slopes of Haleakalā and its volcano wilderness, verdant, remote Hāna with its waterfalls and isolated pools shelters hideaways ideal for quiet contemplation. Upcountry, farmers raise soothing lavender, sweet onions, antioxidant-rich raspberries, and other healing foods. In Maui's leeward south, Wailea's golden beaches offer a haven of sunshine tempered by the trades.

It is said that Maui is home to more practitioners in the healing arts per square mile than any other island. Sybarites can experience their innovative healing approaches in six sprawling luxury resorts that are scattered on all sides of the island.

Entrance to the Spa Hotel Hāna-Maui. (Photo by Thomas Loof)

The Roman Bath at Spa Grande.

The Termé at Spa Grande offers a great prelude to treatments. (Photos courtesy of Grand Wailea Resort Hotel & Spa)

SPA GRANDE

In sunny Wailea in South Maui, in the lee of Haleakalā, the cool and gorgeous Romanesque Spa Grande at the Grand Wailea Resort Hotel and Spa is a destination in and of itself, with its 50,000 square feet of baths, treatment rooms, lounges, rotundas, and marble and slate spaces.

Embracing techniques and traditions from around the world and through the ages, the spa opens at its core to the high-ceilinged Termé Wailea Hydrotherapy Circuit, where you can take to the healing waters of your choice. You may opt for the soothing, water-jet Roman bath with its luxurious, draped lounge beds or a cascading waterfall massage that pummels your hips, calves, and feet with jets of water while a waterfall cascades from ten feet above to massgae your shoulders and neck. You could switch from a relaxing Swiss shower with fifty vertical rotating jets to a warm, stimulating Japanese *furo* with air jets and a cold plunge pool on the side. Or you could try the eucalyptus steam sauna. Central to the Termé, however, are five aromatherapy baths grouped in a semicircle and offering exfoliating papaya enzyme, detoxifying sea salt, nourishing seaweed, essential oils, and balancing Moor mud. Try them all.

An hour of Termé is complimentary when you book a service and makes a great prelude to Spa Grande's treatments. Or you can book the Termé alone and stay as long as you like.

At Spa Grande, all therapies start with a brief polish and sensory delight from the spa's Scrub Bar, a collection of five body scrubs, each said to have a unique healing benefit—the Lavender and Honey scrub enhances peacefulness, for example, while the Pine and Rosemary Scrub brings grounding energies.

Spa Grande also offers select treatments such as an aromatic, velvet-soft rose-petal facial, a deep-moisturizing cocoa butter and vitamin E massage and body wrap, and seasonally inspired themes, such as Vanilla Orchid treatments in spring.

Spa Grande's classes for healing and fitness span the spectrum from volleyball and trampolines to meditation and stress management. Above the spa, an elaborate fitness center sprawls across three equipment rooms for cardiovascular and strength workouts, a studio with a Pilates machine, a basketball court, and an aerobics room. You can even order smoothies here that you are welcome to savor on the spacious oceanfront *lānai*; this relaxation area offers the most serene and peaceful view in the house.

Termé

Hot springs and hot baths have been known for their healing properties since ancient times. In Greece, they were called *thermai*. The comfort-loving Romans, who adopted much of Greek culture and vocabulary, elevated bathing to an art and created the Thermae, lavish marble public baths with arched and thick-walled spaces. Spa Grande has followed the example of contemporary Italian luxury spas with facilities and spelling adjusted to modern trends.

SPA HOTEL HĀNA-MAUI

Secluded from the rest of Maui by the vast slopes of Haleakalā, on green, windward and ocean-front ranching lands at the foot of Ka'uiki Hill—said to be the home of the demigod Maui and the birth-place of Queen Ka'ahumanu—Hotel Hāna-Maui at Hana Ranch embraces the dramatic beauty and naturally healing environment of its surroundings in a tranquil Wellness Center, where each treatment starts with a calming cup of *mamaki* or ginger tea in a private suite.

The intimate spa—just seven treatment rooms plus two rooms for facials—seeks to express the ancient wisdom that true healing and balance must come from the gifts of this earth. It features a large, outdoor basking whirlpool spa surrounded by gardens and adjacent to a reflecting pond, with views of Hāna's coastline and the ocean below—in winter, a favorite spot for whales. Earth tones return in the spa's bamboo floors, Japanese screen doors with handmade fibers, travertine tiles, *'ili 'ili* (small stone) patios, outdoor lava-rock showers, and steam rooms with outdoor cold-plunge pools.

The emphasis is on touch and connection, not technology. And the spa's signature aromatherapy product line, named Honua—"earth" in the Hawaiian language—effuses Hāna's fertile earthiness with scents of sandalwood, ginger, vanilla orchid, and coconut. Tropical and honest, it is said to have a centering, grounding effect. It suits men and women equally.

The pure, powerful Honua oil brings a glow to five signature treatments—a muscle-tension-relieving hot stone massage with *ti* leaves, a cleansing facial and massage, a deeply relaxing aromatherapy bath and massage, a moisturizing scrub and wrap with a scrumptious body butter you do not want to rinse off, and a facial with sensual Honua treatments for feet, hands, and neck.

Spa Hotel Hāna-Maui is home to a Watsu pool, where in saline, warm water you find aquatic renewal with the guidance of a therapist who gently cradles and stretches you. The spa also features numerous therapies that incorporate natural ingredients such as *noni*, *'awa*, spirulina algae, and hydrating muds. Since chances are that you are staying at one of Hotel Hāna-Maui's peaceful cottages—no television, no phones, not even clocks—you may even want to opt for a treatment right on your deck.

Close to the spa are a fitness center and a heated lap pool, both with ocean vistas. The resort offers daily yoga classes, partner-assisted yoga, meditation, and workout hikes. A personal trainer is available.

As for quiet places to heal in solitary contemplation, you are in Hāna—surrounded by verdant earth, waterfalls, surf, lapping waves, and natural pools.

View from Hotel Hāna-Maui at Hāna Ranch. (Photo by Holger Leue)

Mud comes in different colors and textures, such as this mineral-rich green mud made of Colorado Indian Springs clay. It is often blended with aromatherapy oils. (Photos courtesy of Spa Hotel Hāna-Maui)

Wherever clean water and rich soil have touched each other, people have bathed in cooling mud or applied mud masques to rejuvenate the skin. Throughout history, mud has also been used as an effective screen against desert sun. The mud used is a clean, pure, and clay-based substance chosen for is detoxifying powers. Often, it contains the sediment left behind at mineral-rich springs and it may have been absorbed by alluvial soil. It is said to draw out impurities. Mud-lovers claim to feel a tingling extraction while the mud does its work. Soothing and protective, it is also said to stimulate metabolic functions.

Muds come in different colors and textures, from black glaciers and volcanic ashes to green desert clays, white mineral deposits, and red subtropical soils. Often blended with aromatherapy oils, they provide one of the most intimate ways to connect with the nurturing earth.

Pure Earth, Pure Body

Spa Kea Lani

On the east end of Wailea, hugging the little crescent of Polo Beach, the white stucco, Mediterranean-style, suite-hotel—The Fairmont Kea Lani—features sprawling grounds that lead past quiet *koi* ponds and fountain terraces to the glass-door entrance of an exquisite spa, proud of its comfortable elegance.

Nine treatment rooms lie along a curved, green-and-white-tiled hallway. They include a hydrotherapy room with a 75-gallon tub that turns into a fizzy, fragrant, exfoliating bath during Spa Kea Lani's exclusive Citrus Glow. Said to rejuvenate the driest skin, this scrub treatment with tangy, invigorating essential oils and sea salts leaves your body silky soft and lemony scented.

The 'Awapuhi Ginger Treatment is Spa Kea Lani's signature, an offering in celebration of Hawai'i's native ginger. Ground ginger, Maui turbinado sugar, red rose petals, ground orange peel, cornmeal, oats, grapeseed oil, and extracts of green tea and lemongrass come together in a creamy, aromatic, and exfoliating scrub. After a soothing shower, a *lomilomi* massage with *'ili'ili* stones leaves a rich and nurturing balm of ginger butter on the skin: you are ready to be wrapped. While your skin absorbs ginger's warming properties, your therapist treats you to a feet, face, and scalp massage. To prolong this sensually intense experience, you receive some candied ginger and a ginger flower when leaving the spa. With its element of fire, ginger is said to lead you into your true power and authenticity.

Kahina Nui is a facial named after the beautiful goddess Hina, the mother of Maui, and promises—what else—her beautiful glow. It incorporates a lavender-honey polish, a papaya-pineapple massage with *'ili'ili* stones, a seaweed masque, and a deeply relaxing treatment of scalp, hands, and feet.

Couples can choose from a series of packages in which therapists bring the spa to you, in the privacy of your villa or suite.

Spa Kea Lani offers its own locally made line of cleansing, moisturizing lotions and gels in exotic fragrances such as coconut mango, refreshing *liliko'i* (passion fruit) and invigorating rosemary mint. A glass-walled fitness center lies adjacent to the spa, and at the beach you can learn how to paddle Hawaiian outrigger canoes. Outdoor yoga classes, private yoga instructions, and personal training sessions are available.

If you are in search of a quiet meditative space, try the sixth floor foyer, where you can gaze upon the palm-tree-fringed ocean from a wicker chair, while caressed by the breeze.

View of The Fairmont Kea Lani, the location of Spa Kea Lani. (Photo courtesy of The Fairmont Kea Lani Maui)

*Massage by the pool
at the Spa Kea Lani.
(Photo courtesy of
The Fairmont Kea
Lani Maui)*

Meditation

A gentle, quiet method of redirecting the mind to the present moment, meditation has, in one form or another, become a key to spiritual awakening in cultures, traditions, and religions throughout history.

Through concentration, contemplation, or calm refocusing, meditation allows you to return to the here and now. Without attaching any judgments, it intercepts worries about the future and ruminations over the past. It encourages you to develop self-knowledge. Your mind learns to be relaxed yet alert.

Regardless of spiritual or soul growth, however, there is no longer any doubt that a conscious effort to control or still the wandering mind can have tremendous benefits for body, emotions, mental clarity, and brain functioning.

Meditation is a powerful means of managing stress and it triggers the body's physical relaxation response. It helps to disperse negative emotions. It lowers the heart rate, enhances the immune system, and encourages the body's self-healing capacities. It is said to diminish chronic pain, and may aid in the treatment of heart disease. It instills a profound sense of calm and authentic strength.

Not necessarily tied to any creed, and available to anyone, meditation in its simplest form can be a powerful healing practice in which you do nothing more or less than try to follow the rise and fall of the patterns of your breath. In meditation classes, a teacher will gently guide you to the present moment and awareness of your breath with voice, and possibly with music or the gentle sound of Tibetan bells.

Spa Moana

Hugging a long expanse of beach at the foot of the West Maui Mountains, in sunny Kā'anapali, Spa Moana at the Hyatt Regency Maui celebrates foremost its close proximity to the ocean. Its relaxation lounge opens to splendid and calming panoramas with five chaise longues that offer unobstructed, open-air, ocean views. Even its glass-walled salon features this meditative view.

The 15,000-square-foot spa has named its three signature scents Lōkahi, for the harmony and balance that it seeks to impart. Guests at the hotel find the tropical Coconut Mango, Moana Mist with floral ocean breeze fragrance, or refreshing Eucalyptus lotions in their rooms.

Spa Moana's Lōkahi Aromatherapy Massage gives you a choice of tropical essential oils, including locally grown calming lavender, uplifting sweet orange, and cleansing lemongrass.

The cleansing, hydrating power of Brazilian rainforest bee propolis, with its fresh scent of honey, fermentation, and earth, gives a summery splendor to the nearly two-hour-long body treatment Royal Moana.

Said to accelerate healing of the skin, a propolis moisturizer is massaged into the body, which is then covered with heat-preserving linen and towels. Hands and feet also receive a deep hydration with *kukui* nut oil, orange lotion, and a dip in paraffin for maximum effect. A facial with organic ingredients follows. If you skip a shower afterward, the propolis and orange oils continue to moisturize and protect your skin.

Signature treatments also include the Kā 'anapali Salt Glow Scrubs that blend locally made essences and ingredients into a salt-based, invigorating exfoliant. You may choose between warming ginger, stimulating coffee, exotic mango nut, or awakening passion fruit and lime.

Like Spa Moana itself, the Athletic Club with its large glass walls, on ground level, is at the oceanfront. Its equipment comes with private monitors. The adjacent spacious dance studio offers classes in Pilates, meditation, and yoga on oak floors. For the adventurous fitness seeker, a Beach Boot Camp targets cardio-, strength- and flexibility-training with, as equipment and challenge, only nature itself—soft sands, currents, and coconut weights.

A quiet moment at Spa Moana.

View of the pool at Hyatt Regency Maui Resort & Spa.

(Photo courtesy of Hyatt Regency Maui Resort & Spa)

A view from the pool. (Photo courtesy of The Spa at the Four Seasons Resort Maui)

THE SPA AT THE FOUR SEASONS RESORT MAUI

Surrounded by Wailea's beachfront resorts, and secluded even from guests at the Four Seasons, The Spa at the Four Seasons Maui appears like a quiet gem hidden at the back of a healing garden. Sunlight filters into it through long windowpanes that have been interwoven with bamboo. Yet despite the spa's thirteen cool and soothing rooms, most popular are its three thatched oceanside *hale*, complete with lava-rock walls, palm trees, orchids, tropical plants, and tiled floors. Here, you can have evening massages as late as nine o'clock under the stars, with waves lapping just a few feet away.

A favorite outside treatment is the two-hour Hawaiian Temple Bodywork, during which two therapists work in synergy to provide a *lomilomi* massage with coconut and *kukui* nut oil. The trance induced by loving hands, Hawaiian music, and sometimes prayer and chant can be so deep that afterward you may not even know that you turned on the table from your stomach onto your back.

Mele Wailea, "the song of Wailea," is the spa's signature massage. With the aid of heated, fragrant towels wrapped around the neck and placed along the spine to loosen tight muscles, it combines essential aromatherapy oils with a blend of Swedish and *lomilomi* techniques. Your therapist's touch smoothly dances from firm and deep to relaxing, from rocking to still and soft.

For couples, the Wailea Cocoon Experience is an intimate and sensual journey that leaves both you and your partner feeling silky soft and relaxed. In a spacious steam shower you give each other a coconut exfoliant scrub. Then you both slip into a two-person whirlpool tub filled with aromatherapy bath salts and flowers before your therapists come in to massage you each with moisturizing creams—a choice of papaya enzyme, muscle-and-joint-relief aromatherapy, bee propolis, or warm coconut milk. Your massage beds then slowly lower into insulated cushions of warm water until you are submerged, allowing you to float weightlessly in the warmth and security of envelopment. A gentle, guided meditation leads you to a deep sense of relaxation.

Quality is raison d'être at all Four Seasons Resorts. In The Spa at Wailea, it is spiced with the purest ingredients as in the exotic mango, the spa's signature fragrance available in candles, moisturizers, and scrubs. Insistence on quality also shows in a variety of healing elixirs made with Chinese herbs and served alongside the usual chilled water and hot tea. You can sip these tonics in a serene meditation area with sea-grass mats, trickling water, and Zen-inspired elements, either before or after your treatment.

The Four Seasons Resort Maui at Wailea has an outdoor fitness center and tennis courts. In addition to classes such as yoga, tai chi, and meditation, you can even take a session in stress management.

Images from The Spa at the Four Seasons Resort Maui. (Photos courtesy of The Four Seasons Resort Maui at Wailea)

Images from Waihua—A Place of Wellness and The Ritz-Carlton, Kapalua. (Photos courtesy of The Ritz-Carlton, Kapalua)

WAIHUA—A PLACE OF WELLNESS

Once home to chiefs and commoner families, rich in taro *lo'i* nurtured by numerous streams, The Ritz Carlton, Kapalua in West Maui, shelters a small yet exquisite spa named after the ancient Hawaiian concept of *wai hua*. This healing essence of life was the drop of rainwater that came from the heavens and fell directly into the heart of the taro leaf, the Hawaiians' most spiritually symbolic plant. Natural, pure, having never touched the soil, and infused with *mana*, it was invaluable medicine.

Thus, Waihua, the spa, gathers and collects pure essences from nature and keeps its services culturally connected. At the heart of Waihua's treatments are its seven flower essences that seek to heal life's seven most common challenges, and correspond to the seven energy centers of the body. The essences are designed to help with protection, harmony, spiritual awakening, empowerment, stress, family relations, or self-esteem. As an example, Protection contains flower essences from papaya, milo, mango, *pakalana*, and jade vine. The oils are the most concentrated essence of the plants and they carry distinct properties that create their mood-enhancing benefits.

Used as spritzers and in massage oils during Hawaiian treatments, these blends from locally gathered flowers are said to work on many levels, their effect augmented by ritual and chant. Soothing signature therapies include a one-hour Hawaiian Healing Experience as well as three more elaborate packages that might incorporate *pōhaku* or sea-salt exfoliants.

Waihua also offers all-natural face massages such as Maka Hinu, in which locally made essential oils with macadamia nut honey and organic jojoba oil return the glow to your face. All of Waihua's treatments introduce traditional elements, where possible.

Outdoor and ocean-side cabanas are available for singles or couples. Home to Maui's Golf Academy, the resort features golf-specific fitness classes, a fitness center, water workouts, yoga, tai chi, Pilates, hula, hulaerobics (a modern interpretation of hula blended with aerobics), meditation, and even journaling. An early morning walk leads you across the grounds of the Kapalua Resort.

For a quiet, contemplative respite, find a place on the grass near Honokahua, the sacred State Historical Site that fronts the hotel. Here, you can listen to the winds that carry the voice of healing from the elders.

Hawai'i's Big Island

Twice the size of all the other Hawaiian Islands combined, Hawai'i has rightfully earned its nickname, "the Big Island." Yet many also call it the Healing Island, for it is home to five sacred mountains, each with its own transformative gifts.

Cooling snow covers the summit of Mauna Ke'a, with its unobstructed views into the mysteries of the sky. The hot, fiery lava-flows from tempestuous Kīlauea volcano cleanse and purify even as they create new land. The pristine rain forests of Mauna Loa infuse the air with oxygen and shelter the endangered honeycreepers that sing of Hawai'i's unique native past. Kohala's murmuring rivers and myriad waterfalls give sustenance to taro, lychee, and other healthy, healing crops. And to the south of misty Hualālai volcano, overcast evening skies encourage coffee orchards, cocoa pods, and macadamia nut trees to thrive.

Along the sunny, lava-strewn Kona-Kohala Coast, in the leeward cradle of all five mountains, on golden-sand beaches and in calm, clear ocean waters, Hawai'i's royalty relaxed and convalesced long before Honolulu became the seat of government. Powerful freshwater springs provided water just off shore. Cool caves bordered well-traveled trails.

Today, luxury resorts with pools and golf greens occupy these balmy, palm-fringed lands. Caressed by the trades, four resort spas stand out in their celebration of the healing powers of Hawai'i's Big Island.

Golden-sand beaches and calm, clear ocean waters hug the Big Island's Kona-Kohala coast. (Photo courtesy of Hilton Waikoloa Village)

HUALĀLAI SPORTS CLUB & SPA

Bordering the ancient and sunny fishing grounds of Ka'ūpūlehu north of Kailua-Kona, a stone's throw from anchialine ponds that rise with the ocean's tide and are home to native wildlife, the Four Seasons Resort Hualālai blends the spirit of Hawai'i into its service and cultural awareness, and into the treatments and facilities of its spacious Hualālai Sports Club & Spa.

Since you must be a guest or homeowner at the resort to book a spa treatment, the spa experience begins in the Four Seasons' peaceful bungalows—several of which have outdoor lava-rock showers—amid orchids, plumeria, ginger, and ferns. At the spa itself, outdoor massages are given in thatched-roof *hale* (ideal for couples) in the shade of bamboo. The outdoor spa courtyard, with its whirlpool spas, hugs soothing gardens.

Treatment options embrace Pacific cultures and include the gentle, energy restoring touch of Japanese *Reiki*, Thai massage, Ayurvedic treatments, and Chinese acupuncture. Hualālai Sports Club & Spa is most proud of its signature island-themed offerings.

The vanilla- and orange-scented South Seas Sugar Body Scrub starts with warm and cleansing honey from *'ōhi'a lehua* rain forest blossoms that is drizzled softly over your body. Next, the sweet-gritty texture of Hawaiian sugar with nutrient-rich molasses and mild exfoliating enzymes blends with coconut oil, *kukui* nut oil, Vitamin E, and toning aromatherapy oils into a delicious polish, mingling with the honey. After an invigorating Vichy shower that rinses off these sweet ingredients to the last drop and grain—and you never have to leave your table—your skin feels hydrated and soft. An aromatherapy facial massage ending with a tropical-scented moisturizing mist completes this treat.

The spa also features two "local" *wahī*, or wraps. One paints the body with a nutrient-packed, hydrating masque of spirulina, a blue-green algae with powerful antioxidant and detoxifying qualities that is harvested just miles away at Keāhole. The other celebrates the inherently spiritual and uplifting nature of sandalwood, coupled with purifying and energizing lemongrass. Both are said to restore and regenerate the tone—of skin, mind, body, and soul.

The spa is home to a 25-meter lap pool and a fitness center that offers yoga, Pilates, meditation, spinning, hula, fitness assessments, and just about everything else. At Hualālai, the ocean itself is part of the wellness experience: the Alaka'i Nalu, leaders of the waves, teach the Hawaiian arts of surfing and paddling in outrigger canoes. The ocean also practically laps its way into restaurants featuring healthy dishes.

Pilates

Not all mind-body therapies are rooted in ancient tradition. German-born Joseph H. Pilates designed the Pilates method of conditioning in the early 1920s. In 1926, he opened his first studio in New York City, and America's leading dancers soon became devotees, since Pilates improves strength and flexibility without building the bulk associated with weightlifting techniques. Today, it is offered in an increasing number of spas usually as mat classes, although some fitness centers are equipped with the Pilates Reformer apparatus.

Instead of numerous repetitions, Pilates relies on just a few very precise movements that require great control of body and mind, and demand a growing awareness of one's musculature. When done well, Pilates exercises fully engage the so-called "powerhouse" of the body—the abdomen, buttocks, and lower back. As a result, the rest of the body gains greater freedom and fluidity.

Steam as Healer

Steam has been used in healing traditions around the world for thousands of years. Hot vapors are said to increase vitality, promote relaxation, and clear the head. Heat opens the pores of the skin and drives out impurities. It augments the healing effects of herbs. Essential oils diffused in the mists contribute additional therapeutic qualities.

In Polynesian cultures, steam tents were made of kapa cloth. Sometimes, steam lodges were built from lava rocks. The modern steam room is a great preparation for a massage or wrap. The cleansing, antiseptic properties of the eucalyptus oils that are usually added invite you to relax, breathe, and dream. Some spas offer a cold plunge pool adjacent to the steam room. The shock of the extreme contrasts in temperature boosts the circulation and invigorates the body.

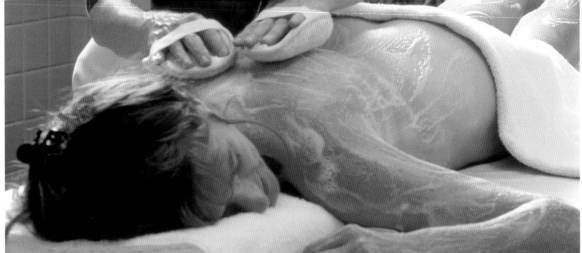

KOHALA SPORTS CLUB & SPA

An oasis within the playful, sixty-two-acre Hilton Waikoloa Village on the northern lava-strewn shores of peaceful 'Anaeho'omalu Bay, Kohala Sports Club & Spa opened in 1988 as the first resort spa in the state of Hawai'i. Ahead of the trend, it opted for a remarkable 25,000 square feet.

There are thirty-two treatment rooms, including three with overhead Vichy showers that are ideal for scrubs and wraps, but its two ocean-side cabanas near the lapping waves are especially alluring.

You may opt for a massage with exotic Body Silk White Orchid Oil, designed exclusively for the spa with its subtle and healing sensuality of the tropics. Made of orchid, jasmine, neroli, and citrus, it is said to have powerful anti-aging properties. A nurturing moisturizer, it gives your skin a silky feel. The Orchid Oil is also available as a Facial Silk. Men might prefer the spa's Malama Kāne massage and facial line with its sandalwood overtones.

Within the spa, both the men's and women's common areas—showers, steam rooms and saunas—open to a semi-outdoor whirlpool spa shaded by lava rocks and tropical plants.

The spa offers two effective ways to relax that take little time. The Big Island Healing Ritual is a gentle way to balance the body with a bath of Hawaiian salts and fragrant, aromatherapy oils. In the soothing, candlelit Hydrosonic Relaxation System room, you'll find yourself massaged "from the inside out" while resting on a vibrating water bed. The therapeutic, deeply relaxing vibrations of calming, soft music (your choice) are said to be amplified through the water mattress, then absorbed by the body.

The spa offers a large variety of treatments from around the world, including a full Ayurvedic menu. Many treatments use tropical ingredients, such as a delicious coconut and mango oil that blossoms in the spa's Coco-Mango Body Wrap. A *ti*-leaf cooling wrap promises to whisk away the heat from sunburned skin.

A room for Pilates and yoga, softened with grass cloth and muslin, looks out over a secluded meditation garden. Tai chi and chi gong are offered. On the other side of the health spectrum are aerobics, resistance balls, racquetball court, fitness center, and championship tennis courts. Consultations and evaluations include fitness, nutrition, body composition, and golf performance. The spa café offers a health-conscious menu.

Steam as Healer. (Photo courtesy of Hilton Waikoloa Village)

Scrub treatment at the Kohala Sports Club & Spa. (Photo courtesy of Hilton Waikoloa Village)

View of the Hilton Waikoloa Village. (Photo courtesy of Hilton Waikoloa Village)

MAUNA LANI SPA

Surrounded by ancient lava flows, and close to Kalahuipua'a's anchialine ponds, the stand-alone Mauna Lani Spa is part of the 3,200-acre Mauna Lani Resort, and merges the Big Island's contrasts of contemporary travel and ancient Hawaiian history, while seeking to connect with Hawaiian culture as much as possible.

The indoor facilities—furnished in mahogany, subtly designed—are sophisticated. You are given a *kīkepa* (sarong) to wrap yourself in, and prepared for the outdoor experience.

A small bamboo grove and three coconut trees form the entrance to the *lā'au* (healing) garden, where a sandy, meandering path lined with sugar cane, ferns, hibiscus, and *hau* trees leads past a relaxing pavilion to nine thatched *hale* supported by unfinished *kiawe* wood. Each secluded *hale* has an outdoor shower.

One even features a Vichy shower for wraps and scrubs. It is quiet, meditative. Protective lava walls both absorb sound and block the wind.

A sheltered circular basalt-stone bench and a low stone table provide the space for the spa's Lava Rock Sauna, where noon temperatures reach 130 degrees. Here, refreshing ice water sipped and poured over your body brings instant pleasure and relief. A bowl of black glacier clay with sandalwood awaits for a self-administered detoxifying body masque. There is no need for a spa therapist.

The spa's Kahi Kīkaha is quite literally its "place to soar." It is a saltwater pool solar-heated to a constant 95 degrees that is specially designed for Aquatic Body Therapy. The Mauna Lani pool is guarded on each side by ancient lava flows and is hidden from view by lava like a shaded fern-fringed grotto.

Lava rock sauna at the Mauna Lani Spa. (Photo courtesy of Mauna Lani Resort)

View of the Mauna Lani Spa. (Photo courtesy of Mauna Lani Resort)

And yes, you actually soar through the water as the therapist glides you effortlessly, stretching and moving you in ways that are impossible on land.

Culturally inspired treatments are important at this spa. There is, of course, the loving, firm touch of *lomilomi* with *pōhaku*. In addition, however, you'll find a *lomilomi hula*, in which the massage movements themselves are performed in choreography with Hawaiian music, and a gentle *'ōpū huli* (belly turn), a soothing tummy massage adapted from Hawaiian therapies—ideal for menstrual cramps, digestion, and other belly pains.

Mauna Lani also features a wide array of other treatments, including its signature Calming Coconilla Experience, a sensuous exfoliation, wrap, and foot massage made with ethereal, calming vanilla, uplifting essential oils of blood oranges, soothing orange rind, and refreshing coconut.

The spa is adjacent to tennis courts, a 25-meter lap pool, and a fitness center with cardiovascular equipment, yoga and Pilates classes, meditation, free weights, and weightlifting machines.

Aquatic Body Therapy

This gentle bodywork is performed in chest-high water that is just below body-temperature with both you and the therapist wearing swimsuits. It is ideal for tight neck, shoulders, and hips because you are almost weightless in the warm water and your muscles put up less resistance. Cradled in one of the therapist's arms with your head above water, you will appreciate the freeing and nurturing feelings that this treatment evokes.

As you close your eyes and surrender to the therapist you will soar, cutting through the water like an agile shark, diving and surfacing like a graceful dolphin and darting in all directions like a school of fish following its leader. You'll twirl, dip, and dance through the water, all the while your muscles will be stretched and massaged. When your feet finally touch ground, it will feel so foreign that you'll want to dive back under.

SPA WITHOUT WALLS

In the royal 'ili of Kalāhuipua'a, close to secret ponds and freshwater springs, Spa Without Walls at The Fairmont Orchid has transformed its spa ambiance to a sensual, outdoor experience that celebrates nature and the peace that comes with relaxing outside in fresh air. An open-air terrace with a Balinese teak pavilion, chaise longues on grassy knolls bordering little streams, and meandering pathways create a true relaxation area. They lead to ten *lauhala*-sided *hale* scattered around tropical gardens, waterfalls, and fish ponds with frolicking *koi* (vividly colored Japanese carp) that are frequented by Tahitian cardinals, little finches, and the occasional plover.

Two of the massage *hale* perch over the fish ponds. If, during your treatment, you turn your head just a little, you can peek through a window in the floor and meditate on the fish swimming by. The spa also offers ocean-side cabanas on the shores of Pauoa Bay, with the sound of lapping waves feet away. Book a massage at one of the ocean-side cabanas an hour before sunset and you can watch for the green flash from one of the Island's best vantage points.

For anything that is on the menu of the Spa Without Walls—and it is extensive—an equivalent out-

Aquatic Body Therapy. (Photo courtesy of Mauna Lani Resort)

Couple enjoying the view at Spa Without Walls. (Photo courtesy of The Fairmount Orchid)

Couple enjoying a massage at Spa Without Walls. (Photo courtesy of The Fairmount Orchid)

Shirodhara, pouring a stream of warm oil on the forehead, is a deeply calming Ayurvedic treatment. (Photo courtesy of The Spa at the Four Seasons Resort Maui)

door treatment exists. For example, a wrap with purifying, mineral-rich Fango (volcanic) mud, inside, can be adapted to a white-clay mud wrap, outside. Complete packages with a series of treatments that include scrubs and wraps can also be experienced outside.

Signature to the spa is its exquisite Vanilla Coffee Exfoliation that blends the aromatic, invigorating stimulus of Kona coffee in a gritty scrub of raw Hawaiian turbinado sugar—said to have antiseptic properties—cornmeal, antioxidant grapeseed oil, smooth *kukui* nut oil, soothing vanilla, and calming, uplifting orange essential oils. After a massage, the scent of pure vanilla lotion lingers on your silky skin for hours.

Spa Without Walls has developed a signature scent for *kāne* (men), *niolopua*, which means "handsome" in the Hawaiian language. It contains *laua'e*, a native fern, soft coconut oils, and a trace of *'iliahi* (sandalwood), which was used in ancient days to scent the *kapa* cloth reserved for chiefs. Although *niolopua* can be used in any of the spa's treatments, it may perhaps find its cultural connection best in a *lomilomi* massage.

The spa features an unusual range of alternative healing approaches such as Healing Touch, Reiki, and Body Talk—non-invasive, light- or non-touch treatments that are said to encourage the body's self-healing abilities. The Spa has steam rooms and saunas, is footsteps away from a fitness center, and offers ocean-side yoga and meditation classes as well as gentle water exercises in the resort's pool.

Ayurveda in the Spa

With its origins in ancient India, Ayurvedic treatments embraces science, spirituality, and religion. Like many Eastern healing traditions, it honors the interconnectedness of all life and the importance of balance and energy-flow. Ayurveda is Sanskrit for "Knowledge of Life."

Health equals harmony, says the Ayurvedic principle. Ayurveda seeks to restore harmony by balancing an individual's metabolic type—a combination of three basic *doshas*: Kapha, Pitta, Vata—with diet, yoga, meditation, medicinal herbs, plant extracts, and massage.

Modern spas have adopted Ayurvedic wisdom. Treatments use warmed oils that contain specialized Ayurvedic herbs, and include massages that are said to open the body's seven energy centers, or *chakras*. Aided by soothing, fragrant, warm, sesame oil, Shirodhara—most common on spa menus—works specifically with the sixth *chakra*, the access point to spiritual insight known as the "third eye," located on the forehead.

Ayurvedic treatments are deeply relaxing and peaceful.

Kaua'i

With its eroded cliffs and steep mountain sides, broad rivers and cascading waterfalls, abundant rainfall and exuberant forests, verdant Kaua'i may well be Hawai'i's most Edenic island. The sight of mists lifting from the purple and rust-hued depths of Waimea Canyon heals the spirit. The taro patches and the National Wildlife Refuge near Hanalei along the rainbow-splashed northern shores infuse one with a sense of peace. Kaua'i's sunny southern beaches soothe anxiety and lift the heart. Rainy Wai'ale'ale, Kauai's highest mountain, reminds us that water truly is the source of life.

Many of the wellness professionals on Kaua'i believe the innate spirituality of the island is its most powerful healing factor. Almost all resorts offer fitness and massage services. Healthy, fresh, and natural foods are available at little cafés and health food stores everywhere.

Mineral-rich mud is said to draw impurities from the skin, while ti leaves draw out excess heat. Photo taken at ANARA Spa. (Photo courtesy of ANARA Spa)

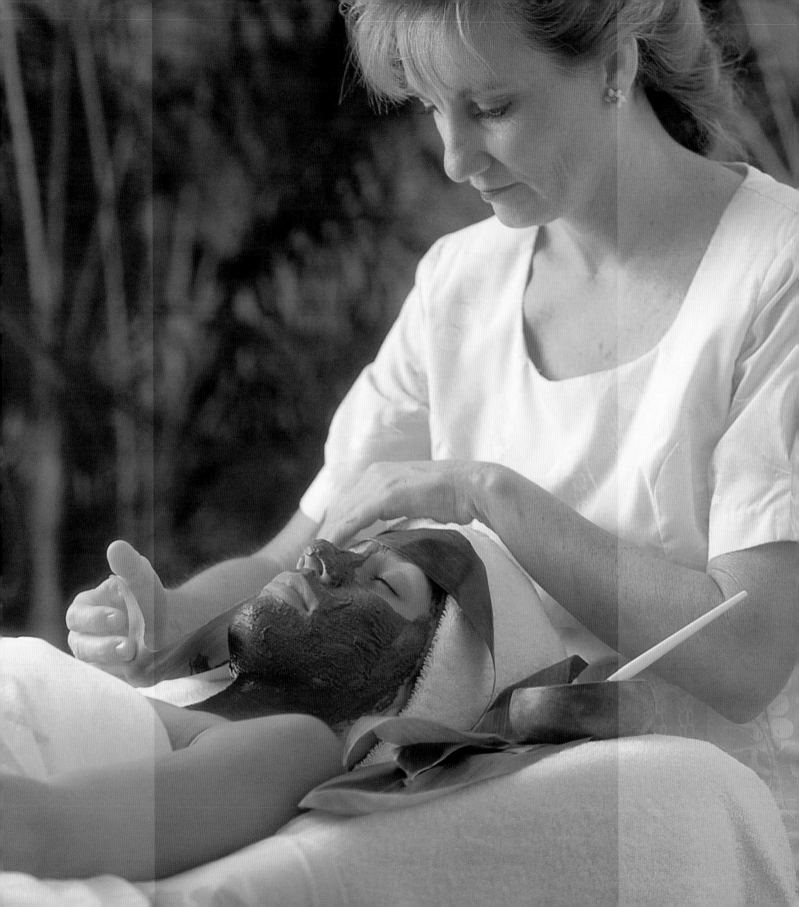

ANARA Spa

Opening onto ancient fishing grounds, in the cradle of the long, sloping sand dunes just west of Makaweli Bluff in Po'ipū, the spacious spa of the Hyatt Regency Kaua'i Resort & Spa embraces the sunny side of the island: 80 percent of its facilities are open-air.

ANARA, which stands for "A New Age Restoration Approach," features lava-rock showers with tropical vines trailing down to your feet. A serene and secluded sunken botanical whirlpool spa awaits, surrounded by orchids and bromeliads. Here, with a soothing candle and a relaxing cup of tea, you can soak away aches and stress with a choice of sea salts, seaweed, calming chamomile, or local aromatherapy blends of wild roses and tropical scents.

Behind a eucalyptus steam room and a Swiss shower with twelve rotating vertical shower heads, ANARA's treatment rooms lie in an organic horseshoe shape around a heated, 25-yard lap pool. They open to private lānai with trickling fountains, palms, gingers, and bamboo.

Couples may opt for an Instructional Massage that not only relaxes both partners, easing sore muscles, but also aims to provide enough hands-on experience to enable guests to take these soothing, healing skills home, along with a guiding booklet and nurturing oil.

The Royal Hawaiian Facial is a signature treatment, carefully adjusted to the type and sensitivity of your skin. It might incorporate detoxifying minerals and seaweed; exfoliating citrus, papaya, and pineapple; mild, nourishing, organic fruit masques; or uplifting sandalwood—popular with men. First, your face is steamed with soft towels, then cooling *ti* leaves ease that last bit of tension. As the *ti* leaves cleanse and purify your skin, a shoulder, neck, hands, and foot massage deepens your relaxation.

ANARA's Body Polish lavishly pampers you with the spa's signature scent, tropical coconut mango, rich with extracts of toning comfrey, soothing chamomile, and a touch of sweet almond oil. Guests at the resort receive a complimentary bottle of coconut mango lotion in their room.

ANARA Spa's fitness center offers yoga, Pilates, tai chi, and sunrise walks as well as personal fitness consultations. For meditation and solitude, the resort's pools meander through a gardenscape of secluded lava formations where you can swim and linger. Pathways lead to the remote and still-wild grass knolls on either side of Po'ipū Beach.

A massage at the ANARA Spa. (Photo courtesy of Hyatt Regency Kaua'i Resort & Spa)

Tai chi classes take advantage of the tranquility of nature. (Photo by Sri Maiava Rusden Photography)

Tai Chi and Chi Gong

From ancient China come two gentle, slow pratices that balance the body, restore *chi* or *qi* (life force), and soothe the mind. Both tai chi and chi gong provide a great sense of well-being.

Chi Gong, which literally means "energy work," uses simple, slow motions coupled with concentrated, controlled, deep breathing. It calms the mind, improves balance, and increases stamina. Its practice in ancient China may well have been a prelude to the more active and complex martial art of tai chi that was said to maintain warriors' agility and clarity of mind.

Tai chi's gentle, deliberate movements require concentration, meditation, and attention to diaphragmatic breathing. A series of twenty to one hundred flowing movements together make a single form that can take up to twenty minutes to perform. Tai chi, with its graceful, soothing motions, is said to harmonize the opposing forces that arise in this world. Tai chi improves balance, strength, and flexibility. It is a powerful stress buster and ideally suited to the elderly.

Lāna'i

At just 141 square miles, and almost always dry and sunny, little, peaceful Lāna'i is one of Hawai'i's most secluded and private islands. Once you roam its red dirt roads in a four-wheel-drive jeep—only thirty miles of Lāna'i's roads are paved—you realize that you have no choice but to leave the stress of a fast-paced lifestyle behind. Lāna'i is about slowing down, playing, and relaxing: there's nowhere to go; you're already here. It offers one luxury spa that in its choice of treatments reflects the essence of this isolated isle.

View of the pool at Mānele Bay Hotel. (Photo courtesy of Castle & Cooke Resorts)

The Spa at Mānele Bay Hotel

Cradling the golden crescent of Hulopo'e Beach where spinner dolphins often play, the elegant Mānele Bay Hotel elevates the quest for health to a lifestyle, for in Lāna'i visitors golf, ride horseback, bicycle, hike, and swim. It's what the island is all about.

Naturally, The Spa at Mānele Bay Hotel excels in soothing sore muscles and body aches. Reminiscent of a Hawaiian plantation home, with calm earth tones and warm, golden hues, decorated in natural stone, bamboo flooring, wicker furniture, koa-framed mirrors, and waterfall features in treatment rooms, the spa allows you to sigh deeply, let go, and relax after playing hard.

Golfers may want to opt for the 19th-Hole Golf Massage, which targets those muscles most often strained on the greens. Educational as well as therapeutic, the treatment ends with specific stretching tips.

In the Big Stretch, your therapist guides you through a series of deep, slow stretches designed to increase awareness of your body's musculature while releasing tension. The spa's therapists recommend that you take some time to warm up in its red-cedar sauna or granite steam room.

The Hehi Lani Royal Foot Treatment—the spa's signature—puts feet first with steaming, eucalyptus-scented towels to warm and relax your feet. Next, there's a scrub with aromatherapy oils, a moisturizing foot massage made of coconut and *kukui* nut oils. To finish, a fragrant essential oil spray is tenderly misted over your feet. Not surprisingly, "Step into Heaven" is the meaning of this treatment's Hawaiian name.

Spa-After-Hours is Mānele's unique way to give couples or small private groups the opportunity to have the entire facility to themselves while being pampered with their choice of massages and treatments and an array of light, healthy food and drink.

Mānele Bay Hotel has a fitness center with cardiovascular and weight equipment. The hotel offers aquatic classes in its shimmering pool, personal training sessions, and even private hula classes. A 90-minute morning hike takes you along old coastal fishermen trails with calming views of the Pacific and the red-dirt hills of uninhabited Kaho'olawe. Yoga classes are available at Mānele's sister property, the Lodge at Kō'ele.

Dining room and aerial view of Mānele Bay Hotel.

Massage at The Spa at Mānele Bay Hotel. (Photos courtesy of Castle & Cooke Resorts)

Nothing equals clear, fresh water to hydrate your body and your skin. (Photo by Sri Maiava Rusden Photography)

Tropical pineapples, mangoes, and papayas are packed with health-giving antioxidants. (Photo by Douglas Peebles)

Island bounty. (Photo courtesy of Hyatt Regency Kaua'i Resort & Spa)

Fresh guavas for fresh and healthful nutrients. (Photo by Ray Wong)

SPA CUISINE

"There is healing in the 'ilima blossoms," Hawaiian wisdom says. Related to the hibiscus, 'ilima

yields a juice that, in ancient days, used to provide medicine for babies with stomach pains. It

would be the first of a myriad of juices, tonics, fresh fruits, and vegetables that this child

would rely on throughout life. To maintain well-being, the Hawaiians relied on a natural

appetite for healing foods.

Indeed, health is intimately entwined with lifestyle, and with the food and drink you choose. The finest spa treatment cannot ensure a radiant complexion, lustrous hair, and glowing skin unless your diet is packed with fresh and healthful nutrients.

Balance and variety are essential, nutritionists say. Health from the inside out is not about fad diets or calorie restriction but about a hunger for the vibrancy and beauty of natural food.

Choose food with color for lots of antioxidants, vitamins, and minerals: broccoli, asparagus, pumpkin, spinach, kale, mustard greens, avocados, strawberries, pomegranates, walnuts, sesame seeds, oranges, guavas, papayas, beets. And, drink fresh water—tall glasses of it—to hydrate your body, including your skin.

With a balmy climate and just the right amount of rainfall, the Hawaiian Islands produce an abundance of colorful foods. Healthy nutritional choices are easier and more fun than ever before. Island chefs have created an entire cuisine based on fresh, locally grown ingredients that honor the many cultures that have each brought their flavors and their foods. Splendid dishes flavored with lemongrass, kaffir lime leaves, and ginger do not need salt or heavy sauce. Macadamia nuts with heart-healthy oils provide crunch. Buttery avocados add a silken creaminess that enhances other flavors. Papayas, mangoes, pineapples, Maui onions, Kahuku corn, and fresh cilantro combine in tangy-sweet relishes that accompany fresh grilled island fish. And of course, the taro plant, *kalo*, the staple of ancient Hawaiian life and one of the pillar ingredients of Pacific Rim cuisine, lends its starchy, earthy flavor and unique texture to stir-fries, breads, and traditional dishes such as poi. The tasty, heart-shaped leaves of the taro plant are used to wrap steamed fish and meats, and flavor a variety of dishes.

In their synergy of compounds known as phytochemicals (for which science continues to discover new properties) certain island foods stand out for their inherent and specific healing abilities. These are the foods that calm, cleanse, invigorate, tone, or soothe—unrivaled spa

Spicy ginger root soothes an upset stomach and boosts energy. (Photo by Ray Wong)

Fish and poi, rich in protein and minerals, are traditional dishes in the Islands. (Photo by Douglas Peebles)

foods that lend themselves to silken smoothies, colorful juices, and fragrant herbal teas.

It is fairly simple to make infusions, smoothies, and health drinks at home. Many island ingredients are available at ethnic markets throughout the United States.

Invest in a blender, and toss in sweet papaya, smooth, velvety banana, and a dash of lime. Add some nonfat yogurt, protein powder, honey, or soy milk to taste.

Making your own vegetable juice has become easier with powerful juicers. Experiment with earthy and vitamin-rich beets, sweet, skin- and eye-nourishing carrots, or intense, tangy spinach leaves packed with iron.

And what is more soothing than to sip your way to health with a dreamy tea or tisane brewed in a beautiful pot? Tea as a ritual is an island tradition dating back to Asian immigrant days, a lingering reminder to practice mindfulness. The ceremony itself—heating the water, measuring the leaves, brewing—is an antidote to stress. Most resort spas offer their own serenity blends made with carefully selected herbs, leaves, flowers, and spices—pick up a tin and bring it home, or experiment with your own tea combinations.

Island spas take advantage of an abundance of island produce. Try these recipes straight from the kitchens of resort spas to yours whenever you crave a tropical treat.

Both green and black teas provide powerful antioxidants and lift the spirit.

The right tools aid in transforming an ordinary cup of a tea into a ritual of mindfulness.

Papayas contain stress-busting magnesium and potassium. (Photos by Ray Wong)

Ingredients for Smoothies and Juices

A radiant glow comes from citrus fruit packed with vitamin C. (Photo by Sri Maiava Rusden Photography)

Tart, refreshing lemon and lime. (Photo by Ray Wong)

Watermelon, the ideal thirst quencher... (Photo by Sri Maiava Rusden Photography)

BANANA (MAIʻA)

Brought to Hawaiʻi by the early Polynesian voyagers, with bright green, broad-leafed foliage that fans out from herb-like stalks, banana trees flourish on all the islands, in numerous varieties. A tonic made from the sap of nipped flower buds was said to treat listlessness. The banana is a nutritious food, rich in fatigue-fighting potassium and magnesium. Its carbohydrates trigger serotonin production, and it is therefore considered a calming food.

STARFRUIT

The carambola is nicknamed "starfruit" for its fluted shape that in cross-section makes a star. This pretty, tender yellow fruit grows in the backyard of many Asian family homes and can be found on Hawaiʻi roadside fruit stands in summertime. Sweet, slightly acidic, succulent, and crisp, starfruit is said to be a diuretic, and is a cooling, refreshing thirst-quencher on hot, tropical days.

GUAVA

Jellies and jams made with this delicious fruit fill market shelves island-wide. Indeed, the hardy tree grows wild along roadsides, and is used to fence off pastures. Guava fruit is high in vitamin C, especially in the skin. Its bright pink color indicates the presence of free radical–fighting antioxidants.

HONEY

Mentioned for its therapeutic benefits in Egypt as early as 1500 BC, honey has powerful antibacterial qualities, eases sore throats, and is said to encourage the body's natural healing mechanisms. Hawaiʻi is home to wild bees that produce distinctly flavored honeys from macadamia nut or *kiawe* flowers, and from *lehua*, the blossoms of the native ʻōhiʻa tree that thrives on Pele's volcanic slopes. A natural sweetener that has captured the essence of the sun, honey also contains antioxidants.

Bananas
Guava
Honey
(Photos by
Ray Wong)

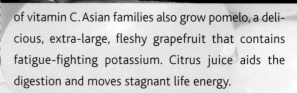

MANGO

The tiny blossoms and heavy-hanging green, red, and golden fruits of mango trees are a most welcome sight to islanders. Mangoes are pickled when green—pit and all—savored when ripe, fresh, and juicy, and when there is an abundant crop, dried or made into chutney and added to sweet and savory foods. Mangoes are packed with cell-protecting beta-carotene. They contain potassium, magnesium, and digestive enzymes.

CITRUS: POMELO, ORANGE, GRAPEFRUIT, LIME

The citrus family proliferates in Hawai'i and was prized by merchant sailors in the nineteenth century for its ability to ward off scurvy during long voyages, which we now attribute to the presence of lots of vitamin C. Asian families also grow pomelo, a delicious, extra-large, fleshy grapefruit that contains fatigue-fighting potassium. Citrus juice aids the digestion and moves stagnant life energy.

PAPAYA

A breakfast or smoothie in Hawai'i often includes half a papaya, rich in vitamin C and digestive enzymes. Its deep orange color reveals an abundance of beta-carotene. Papayas also are a good source of stress-busting magnesium and potassium. Farmer's markets may sell strawberry papaya, lauded for its red color and berry-sweet, juicy taste.

PASSION FRUIT

The name of this native of tropical America refers to nothing less than the passion of Christ, for the crown-like complexity of the purple and white blossoms that adorn this strong vine. Its fruit yields an intense, fragrant juice prized in sorbets, smoothies, and condiments. Rich

in vitamin C, the deep orange color also indicates the presence of cell-protecting carotenoids.

PINEAPPLE

While remaining a significant island plantation crop, the tart, white to deep-yellow bromeliad fruit is making a comeback in cleansing juices that aid the digestion. Pineapples contain stress-busting magnesium, and are also a good source of vitamin C.

SPIRULINA

A nutrient-rich, blue-green algae produced at the Natural Energy Laboratory of Hawaii Authority in Keāhole on the sunny Kona Coast, spirulina is often used as a powder to enrich smoothies and juices with minerals, vitamins, and proteins. Just one tablespoon daily provides healthy amounts of essential fatty acids. Its detoxifying properties are said to ease anxiety, depression, and irritability.

WATERMELON

Grown primarily on the small island of Moloka'i, juicy, sweet, local watermelons are served in generous wedges at barbecues and cookouts across the state. Nothing makes for a finer thirst quencher in hot weather. The red flesh of the watermelon is cooling and is a good source of lycopene, an antioxidant associated with cancer prevention and brain protection.

Mango
Citrus
Papaya
Passion Fruit
Pineapple
Watermelon

(Photos by Ray Wong)

Tea

GINGER

Ginger root, the spicy, hot, pungent element of chai tea, is an essential ingredient in Asian and Pacific Rim cuisine. Hawai'i is the only state in the nation to grow it commercially. Ginger tea (simmer one cup of water with one or two crushed slices for about ten minutes) relieves nausea and soothes upset stomachs. It heats the body, increases the blood flow, and boosts energy.

GREEN TEA

Although not produced in the islands in significant quantities, green tea has long been an integral part of Hawai'i's cultural Asian traditions. Mild, slightly astringent, with hints of fresh-grass sweetness, green tea provides powerful antioxidants associated with a reduced risk of certain cancers. It is said to lower blood cholesterol levels and acts like a digestive and toner. It contains just enough caffeine to boost lagging energy and it lifts the spirit.

LEMONGRASS

Lemony-sharp, with summer-green overtones, lemongrass enhances many Asian dishes with its elusive flavor. Cut into paper-thin slivers, its white-green ringed bulbous base is a favorite in Hawai'i regional cuisine. Deeply aromatic, lemongrass soft-

Sip your way to health with a tea brewed in a beautiful pot.

Ginger
Green Tea
Lemongrass

(Photos by Ray Wong)

*Hibiscus
Kava
Māmaki*

*Green tea, freshly
brewed, tastes
slightly astringent
yet reveals scents of
summer-grass
sweetness. (Photos
by Ray Wong)*

ens bitter flavors, blends especially well with green tea, and has toning, calming, and cleansing qualities.

HIBISCUS

Tangy, exotic, tropical, the bright crimson-tasseled blossoms of this sun-loving shrub make for a toning, cooling tea, deliciously refreshing when poured over ice. Hibiscus flowers are said to aid in lowering blood pressure.

KAVA

A handful of *'awa* bars in Hawai'i serve this traditional Pacific Island beverage in large bowls, brewed fresh from the bitter astringent root and sweetened only with guava juice or coconut. A tingling feeling in the mouth quickly spreads and brings an overall sense of deep relaxation and well-being. Equally effective in its milder forms, in teas available in health food stores, kava relieves anxiety, induces restful sleep and calms body and mind.

MĀMAKI

When dried, the broad white-backed leaves of this native shrub, a member of the nettle family, make a favorite Hawaiian tea that has been enjoyed since ancient times. Earthy, reminiscent of rain forests, it strengthens and gives energy.

Refreshing Drink Recipes

GOLDEN WAILEA SPA-TINI.

With digestive enzymes, balancing minerals, nourishing protein, and a hint of citrus-scented honey, this elegant smoothie staves off hunger pangs. It is made in the fitness center of Termé Wailea.

1 full slice	Pineapple
1	Banana
1/2 cup	Low-fat yogurt
1/4 cup	Guava juice
1/2 Tsp.	Tangerine-blossom honey

Combine well in blender. Makes two Spa-tinis.

Courtesy of Termé Wailea at the Grand Wailea.

KONA BREEZE

Rich in calming, balancing potassium, cell-protecting antioxidants, vitamin C, and soothing honey, this drink can be the perfect start to a peaceful day.

1	Banana
1	Orange
4 ounces	Passion orange juice
4 ounces	Guava juice
2 Tbsp.	Honey
Ice	

Combine well in cocktail blender. Serves two.

Courtesy of Kohala Sports Club & Spa.

KUPONO SPECIAL

Papaya balances the digestive system, and watermelon has a cooling effect. This juice is a good source of beta-carotene, vitamin C, and the antioxidant lycopene, a powerful cell protector.

1/2	Papaya
Juice of 1	Lime
1 wedge	Watermelon

Combine well in blender. Serves one.

Courtesy of Kupono Café at the ANARA Spa, Hyatt Regency Kaua'i Resort & Spa.

SHIPWRECK ZINGER

Packed with vitamins A and C, this spicy, energizing juice is an ally in cancer prevention and in lowering blood cholesterol. The ginger root warms the body and stimulates digestion and appetite.

1	Carrot
1	Apple
1/2 inch	Peeled, fresh ginger

Juice in vegetable juicer. Serves one.

Courtesy of Kupono Café at the ANARA Spa, Hyatt Regency Kaua'i Resort & Spa.

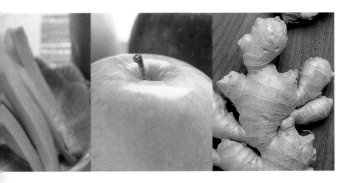

PAPAYA GINGER STING

Warming, spicy, and tangy-sweet, this tropical drink will settle an upset stomach and is packed with vitamins A and C. As a non-alcoholic cocktail, its sheer fizzy elegance gives mai tais and daiquiris a run for their money.

1	Large papaya—
	peeled, seeded, and cut into chunks
1/4 cup	Honey
1 1/2 Tbsp.	Fresh lime juice
1 Tsp.	Grated, fresh ginger
Dash	Angostura bitters
10 ounces	Cold sparkling water
Crushed ice	

Purée papaya, honey, lime juice, ginger, bitters and two ounces of the sparkling water in a blender. Transfer to pitcher. Blend in remaining water. Serve over crushed ice. Serves two.

Courtesy of The Fairmont Kea Lani.

(Photo of water courtesy of the Mandara Spa)

(Photos of ingredients by Ray Wong)

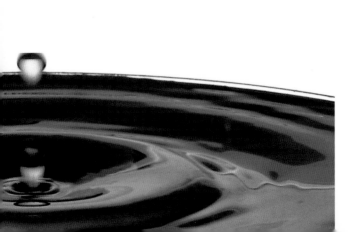

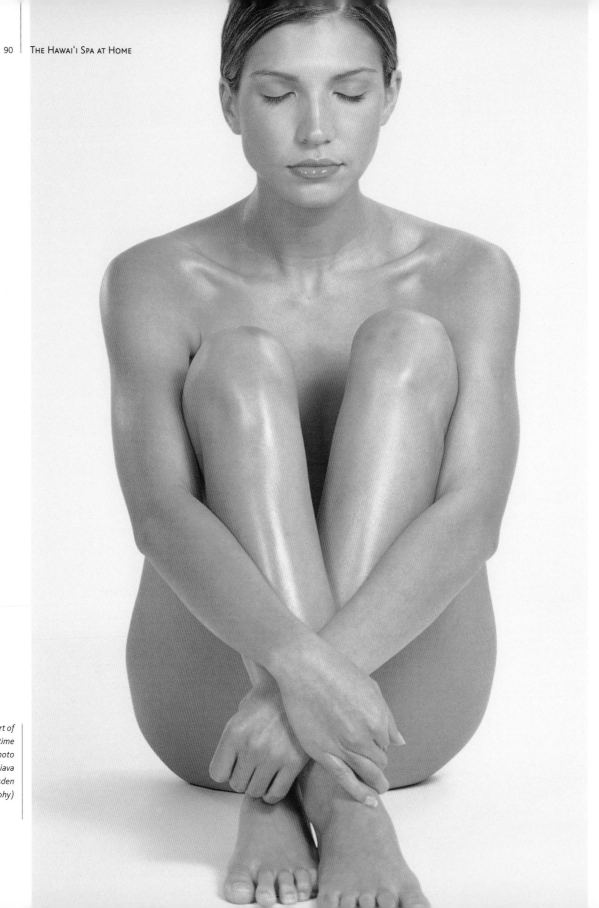

The sensual art of relaxation, a time for you... (Photo by Sri Maiava Rusden Photography)

THE HAWAI'I SPA AT HOME

The sounds of lapping waves. The scents of plumeria, white ginger, and maile. Ocean salt carried on the breeze. A lingering taste of papayas and mangoes bursting with flavors of the sun. The silken feel of coconut oil on warm skin. Soothing images of verdant ferns and gently swaying palms. These are the gifts of the Hawaiian Islands.

Hundreds of years before the advent of luxury spas, the Hawaiian people revered such natural gifts. Using them wisely, they knew well how to restore a sense of balance, peace, and relaxation. With meditation, chant, and prayer, they sought wellness and health. Massage, herbal medicine, and the healing touch were deeply respected skills, passed on from generation to generation. At times of celebration, or when great endurance or clarity of mind was called upon, men and women anointed themselves with rich *kukui* nut oil. They scented their *kapa* cloths with *'iliahi* and *maile* leaves. They rubbed coconut oil in their hair to protect it from the sun. They held sacred the life-giving snow of Poli'ahu, the goddess who filled rivers and bathing ponds with fresh water from her home, the summit of Mauna Kea.

In times of peace and natural harmony, the land, the *'āina*, offered itself as a vast nurturing, healing source. The Hawaiian people were careful stewards of the gifts that nature bestowed. The art of relaxation blended with respect and awareness in a dance that interconnected the pleasures of humans with the forces of water, wind, sun, and earth.

Ultimately, it is this dance between nature and the human spirit that is integral to the modern spa in Hawai'i. It makes these spas different from spas anywhere else in the world. The specialness of spas in Hawai'i has less to do with the technical details of an exfoliation, or the exact replication of a body polish formula, than with natural ambiance and a respectful use of natural gifts and ingredients.

The diverse experiences of the island spa all have a root in the islands' elements, their rich abundance, and their natural sensuality. Island-style, the spa can ground us, bring us back to center, and help us to heal.

With little effort and small expense you can create your own island spa experience at home—wherever you live. Your tropical spa can be any place in your house or garden that you can infuse with serenity, and that in turn, can transform and rejuvenate you.

Just a few ingredients can set the mood. You may want to listen to relaxing island music. If you like tea, stock up on a few island teas. Appendix III provides suggestions to get you started. You may want to dim the lights for a calming sensuality that whispers of warm, tropical nights, or in contrast, create a sun room where the nurturing warmth and clarity of golden rays has the power to uplift.

Experiment with candles. Aromatherapy candles come in many scents, including earthy, balancing *maile*, sweet-tropical coconut-mango, and spicy, warming ginger. These

The scent of lavender calms the mind and tones the nervous system.

Aromatherapy candles set the mood.

Plant-based oils and lotions with natural ingredients are easily absorbed by the skin.

Fragrant gardenia wrapped in ti leaf.

(Photos by Ray Wong)

are available via the Web sites of Hawai'i spas. The spas also use calming lavender scents and refreshing mints. Choose candles made with natural beeswax or vegetable wax and pure essential oils. The smoke from artificial chemicals, including paraffin wax, can be harsh on throat and skin.

You may want to surround yourself with a few tropical plants. Orchids are widely available, as are certain vine and fern species. They grow wild in Hawai'i's climate. In your home, they create an oxygen-rich island ambiance.

Spa treatments can be as elaborate or simple as you wish. You can order creams, lotions, and oils from spa Web sites, or experiment with your own blends.

For a nurturing massage oil, you'll want something natural—emollient, protective *kukui* nut or coconut oils are excellent choices. *Monoi tiare* from Tahiti is a pure coconut oil scented with Tahitian gardenia, infinitely tropical and widely available.

Regardless of the oil you choose make sure it is plant-based. In their own ways, plant oils carry within them the healing, warming powers of the sun. After all, they are pressed from the seeds that created them with the aid of light and warmth in order to provide sustenance to new life. They are packed with beneficial fatty acids. The skin easily absorbs these rich oils. Hair takes on beautiful luster when conditioned with them. Mineral oils, from the cold depths of the earth, are harder to absorb; they lie on top of the skin and seal it off from the air.

A FOOTBATH TO LIGHTEN YOUR STEP

Quietly ignored unless they hurt, usually stuffed into tight socks and ill-fitting shoes, our faithful feet carry our entire body-weight for thousands of miles over the course of a lifetime, to—and through—all the busy projects and destinations that we can dream up. They rarely complain under their burden, yet how good they feel when we spend deliberate time relaxing them.

In ancient Hawai'i, the feet were considered precious. Hawaiian royalty as well as Hawaiian commoners walked barefoot along coastal trails, enjoying the contact with sun and soil. Their feet endured jagged lava rock, then found soothing comfort in the sea. Naked feet trampled the mud in taro patches and welcomed the morning dew on wet grass. The soles of the feet delineated the body and connected it with the earth and the gods. Feet were bathed, massaged, and oiled to better meet the tasks at hand.

Even today, children born and raised in the islands often go barefoot. Island *keiki* know the warmth of white sand, the coolness of green grass, the heat of dusty roads, and the salt of the ocean on the soles of their feet.

Before entering a home in Hawai'i, islanders remove their shoes. At beachfront homes, a foot bath is often available to rinse off sand that might have crept into sandals. In these symbolic gestures, you leave behind the worries of the world. You enter a sacred space, and express respect for its cleanliness. Many spas in Hawai'i honor Hawaiian tradition and offer a foot bath or foot ritual at the beginning of a massage.

At home, you can ensure healthy island feet with massages that exert gentle pressure on the soles. Go barefoot whenever you get a chance, especially in the garden or on natural, wooden floors. Massage moisturizers into the skin, and make time for pampering foot baths to soothe aching, tired feet.

Sharon Warren, who designs natural products and product lines for numerous island and mainland spas from her home on the slopes of Hualālai Volcano on the Big Island, provides this recipe for a foot bath, island-style:

1 Tbsp.	Sea salt
1 Tsp.	Coconut oil
4 drops	Pure, organic vanilla extract
	Fresh flowers

Mix ingredients and add to warm foot bath. Sprinkle with flowers. Soak feet for ten minutes. Coconut oil—the versatile island ingredient—softens your skin and eases aching muscles. Sea salt purifies the skin and nourishes it with minerals. Vanilla calms and relaxes the mind. Fresh flowers make the bath a celebration. Follow this treatment with a *kukui* nut oil massage.

Foot refreshment.
(Photo courtesy of
ANARA Spa)

A Calming and Purifying Bath

In Hawai'i, baths are not just to cleanse; they are also meant to relax. In the humid heat of summer days, the ancient Hawaiians bathed with 'awapuhi kuahiwi, soapy, wild ginger flowers that flourished near jungle ponds and waterfalls. It was a cooling, refreshing way to reconnect with the land.

The power of salt water played an equally important role. On all islands, shallow shoreline pools were used for healing baths.

During the sugar plantation era of the late 1800s and early 1900s, Asian immigrant laborers soaked off tension, anxiety, aches and pains in *furo*, square wooden tubs filled with steaming water, introduced by the Japanese. The *furo* did more than ease physical pain; it was said to cleanse mental impurities.

Almost all of Hawai'i's spas offer soothing, aromatherapy baths, and some, like SpaHalekulani and Spa Grande even have a *furo*. Flowers drift lazily in the fragrant, and often mineral-rich water. Music plays softly. The sound of waterfalls whispers in the background.

Such leisurely tropical baths are easily replicated at home: add a few drops of essential oils to your bath water and let the vapors slow you down. After your bath, massage a moisturizing lotion into your skin.

Ginger warms the body, improves circulation, and soothes aching muscles.

Citrus invigorates, refreshes, and revives.

Lemongrass tones the body and calms the emotions and the mind.

Jasmine feels sensuous and uplifts the spirit.

Lavender, mixed with a tablespoon of *kukui* nut oil, softens the skin and summons sleep.

Add flowers and make your own tropical bath. (Photo courtesy of Mandara Spa)

FOR A SMOOTH AND SILKEN BODY: 'AWAPUHI GINGER SCRUB

When mixed with a soothing, emollient oil and a healing essential oil, finely gritty ingredients—sea salt, sugar, cornmeal, or coffee grounds, for example—become effective exfoliants that remove the skin's outer layer of dead, rough cells, revealing the fresh, new layer underneath. Such polishes and scrubs leave the skin hydrated, soft, and supple.

Plant-loving Hawaiian spas incorporate a wide variety of tropical ingredients for their invigorating scrubs. Ginger root is said to aid digestion. It warms the body, and gets the blood flow going. Raw turbinado sugar, an unrefined product from the sugar plantations and rich with minerals, has also been gratefully adopted. It is grainy like sea salt, yet feels milder and less astringent when rubbed into the skin. Hawaiian honey nurtures and protects. Here's an exfoliating scrub inspired by Spa Kea Lani's signature treatment at the Fairmont Kea Lani. It whispers of Maui's lush valleys and its sole sugar plantation—one of just two still operating in the islands.

1 Tbsp.	Grated fresh ginger or ground ginger powder
1 Tbsp.	Raw sugar
1 Tbsp.	Cornmeal
1 Tbsp.	Ground oats
1 Tsp.	Honey
3 Tbsp.	Grapeseed oil

Mix all the ingredients. Wet your skin. Massage the paste gently over your body, then shower off.

Variation: Use ground coffee instead of ginger for a stimulating scrub.

Ingredients for the 'Awapuhi Ginger Scrub. (Photo by Ray Wong)

TROPICAL FRUITS POLISHER

Everyone loves the refreshing taste of Hawai'i's brightly colored, carotene-rich papayas and pineapples—but you will also love what their digestive enzymes and gently exfoliating acids can do to your skin. Spa Olakino *Salon puts fruits in the blender minutes before treatments. You can do the same with this skin-polishing, vitamin-packed formula.

1	Papaya
1/8	Pineapple
1/2 cup	Cornmeal

Purée papaya and pineapple in blender, then mix with cornmeal. Massage all over the body. Rinse off in warm shower.

Papaya is a welcome ingredient in island-style spa formulas. (Photo by Ray Wong)

FOR A GLOW: HYDRATING TROPICAL FACE OIL

Exposed to the elements more than any other part of the body, yet also the most expressive part of you, your face deserves special care. The soaps, lotions, and potions that serve the rest of the body just fine may be too harsh for the thin, delicate facial skin already battered by sunshine, pollutants, and free radicals. Hawaiian women used gentle *kukui* nut oil to pamper their faces.

Warren Botanicals has created a formula that incorporates antioxidant grapeseed oil, nourishing macadamia nut oil, and hydrating, toning, gently stimulating essential oils.

1/2 ounce	*Kukui* nut oil
1/4 ounce	Macadamia nut oil
1/4 ounce	Grapeseed oil
3 drops	Jasmine essential oil
3 drops	Neroli essential oil
2 drops	Rose geranium essential oil
2 drops	Lemon essential oil

Combine all ingredients in a one-ounce amber glass bottle with dropper, apply four drops on clean face and neck, morning and night.

Tropical face oil Ingredients. (Photo by Ray Wong)

LUSTROUS LOCKS

Hawaiian women appreciated their beautiful, glossy hair. They took good care of it. Men, too, kept their hair clean and oiled. Warriors were known to wear it short.

In showers of cool waterfalls, the fragrant, crushed *maile* leaves and the sudsy gel that oozes from *'awapuhi kuahiwi* (wild ginger) made for refreshing, cleansing shampoos. To condition and soften the hair, and to give it its prized luster, coconut and *kukui* nut oils were massaged into the scalp.

Kohala Sports Club & Spa at the Hilton Waikoloa Beach Resort adds sensual ylang ylang to its oil conditioner that also soothes the scalp. Ylang ylang is said to balance naturally oily hair. Warren Botanicals created this intensely fragrant, garden-like formula:

1/2 ounce	Coconut oil
1/2 ounce	Jojoba oil
4 drops	Ylang ylang essential oil

Mix the ingredients. Apply to dry, clean hair and gently massage into scalp and through hair. Wrap a warm towel around the head. Let the mixture penetrate for at least 20 minutes, then rinse and shampoo.

Long, flowing hula girl hair. (Photo by Douglas Peebles)

FEELING REFRESHED IN BODY AND SOUL

In Hawai'i, a soft, sudden spray of fresh, cool rain from river or ocean, whipped up by gentle trade winds, brings instant relief on hot, sticky days when a swim or soak is out of reach. The mountain mists that meander into valleys during the late afternoon bring rejuvenation and a sense of sacredness.

No matter where you are, a fine mist of fragrant water gives a tired body new energy and clears a fatigued mind. When healing ingredients are added, body mists are said to reach even the soul.

Green tea, which came to the islands with Asian immigrants, has been adopted by the spas for its longevity-enhancing properties. In this body mist formula, Mandara Spa at the Hilton Hawaiian Village Beach Resort & Spa adds toning, stimulating, and energizing citrus oils to green tea's antioxidant properties. You can adapt the formula. Lavender oil, for example, would give you a calming mist. Rose would soothe and add a hint of romance. Rosemary invigorates and inspires the mind. To get you started:

1 cup	Green tea
2 drops	Lemon essential oil
2 drops	Lime essential oil

Mix the ingredients in a pump spray bottle and cool in refrigerator. Shake before use. Mist lightly on face and body after bathing and toweling off.

Cooling ocean spray lifts the spirit and boosts energy. (Photo by Douglas Peebles)

Citrus oils stimulate and invigorate. (Photo by Ray Wong)

SOOTHING SUNBURN

In Hawai'i, sunshine is a way of life. The warmth of the sun feels nourishing and healing, and provides the body with much-needed vitamin D. But with too much sun, visitors and *kama'āina* (locals) alike can end up with a painful burn. If you don't have an aloe plant growing on your back porch from which you can squeeze a little soothing gel, rely on this effective recipe that uses aloe, available in health food stores, and lavender, whose essential oil is frequently used in Europe for any type of burn.

4 ounces	Pure aloe vera gel
20 drops	Lavender essential oil

Mix and apply to sunburned skin.
Courtesy of Warren Botanicals.

The spiky, succulent aloe leaves release a cooling gel. (Photo by Ray Wong)

Essential oils heal the skin and lift the spirit. (Photo by Ray Wong)

SMOOTHING OUT THE CELLULITE

We are not aware of any treatments that Hawaiian women might have relied upon to banish cellulite. But if it is true that a healthy diet combined with regular exercise is one of the most effective ways to prevent or lessen these ungainly fatty deposits on the hips and thighs, then Hawaiian women were doing everything right. Taro, breadfruit, and lean fish were dietary staples, and their lifestyle was abundantly active. Contact with the West introduced vitamin-rich citrus fruits whose stimulating oils are said to tone the skin and to get stagnant energies moving. Citruses work hard in this delicious citrus-based cellulite formula, created by Warren Botanicals.

4 ounces	Grapeseed oil
6 drops	Cypress essential oil
7 drops	Juniper-berry essential oil
7 drops	Fennel essential oil
10 drops	Orange essential oil
10 drops	Lemon essential oil

Mix together in a four-ounce amber glass bottle. Apply daily, preferably in the morning. Dry brush cellulite areas and apply cellulite oil. Great to apply before exercise.

MADE FOR MEN

Spicy, refreshing, toning, energizing, the recipe for Tropical Spice After Shave requires quite a selection of ingredients, including stimulating fresh rosemary leaves and cleansing green cardamom pods. We included this treat because men love the spa as much as women do, and yet natural, homemade formulas for men remain all too rare.

1 cup	Witch hazel
2	Bay leaves
3 pods	Green cardamom (bruised)
2 sticks	Cinnamon
12	Cloves
2 two-inch sprigs	Fresh rosemary
6 one-inch strips	Fresh lemon peel
8 drops	Orange essential oil
1 Tsp.	*Kukui* nut oil
1 Tsp.	Vegetable glycerin

Combine all ingredients in a sixteen-ounce jar. Store in a dark place, shaking daily for two weeks. Strain. *Courtesy of Warren Botanicals.*

Spice up your daily grooming ritual. (Photo by Sri Maiava Rusden Photography)

Ingredients for an After Shave: Cinnamon, bay leaves, lemon peel, rosemary, cloves. (Photo by Ray Wong)

How to Spa

A slender woman of nubile age relaxes in a whirlpool spa, her face serene, her movements languid, her skin moist and smooth, hibiscus blossoms like an afterthought caressing her pedicured feet. A flirtatious dance of bubbles envelops her.

If advertisements and magazine spreads are to be believed, the spa is the exclusive playground of the eternally beautiful and female young, shrouded in the damp mists of mystery. That can be a little intimidating for the rest of us. And, of course, it is *not* the truth. The spa and the spa experience are for everyone.

Fortunately, the spa staff and the scientific community know that modern spas help us relax and heal. Relaxation is essential to good health. The spa, in its primary function, reduces stress—and these days, stress affects everyone.

Stress contributes to America's leading causes of death, including heart disease. It is not merely a buzzword, or something we "just have to get used to" as part of progress and a high-tech world. Stress is real, and when sustained over months or years, it is dangerous.

Stress produces certain chemicals, including cortisol, that help the body in an emergency to fight or flee. An animal, ready to pounce on its prey, is under stress. A firefighter in a burning building is under stress. Stress pushes the body into high alert. Ready to hold on for dear life, the blood pressure rockets, the blood vessels and throat constrict, the muscles tighten,

Ahhh, the spa.
(Photo by Sri Maiava
Rusden Photography)

and the breath becomes shallow and fast. With stress, the immune system weakens, the brain loses the ability to think things through, metabolism changes, and restful sleep becomes impossible.

A spa to the rescue. Gentle treatments and techniques that tell body and mind that all is well return us to our natural well-being. They rebalance chemicals and lead the body away from a state of permanent "fight-or-flight" to long-term wellness.

The essence of the spa is in the basics: the power of healing touch. No one quite understands why prolonged, gentle touch is so vital to well-being and why it relaxes us so much, yet plenty of scientific evidence suggests that it soothes the entire being in most effective healing ways.

A calm mind heals body and soul; a relaxed body clears the mind. Mind–body medicine explores the interdependent connection between physical health and the perceptions and messages of the mind. Any spa that takes itself seriously must keep current with the latest research. Discoveries that center on the healing potential of touch, human interaction, and good intent are pouring in. Soothing scents, soft music, calming colors, fabrics soft to the touch, all play a relaxing role. In addition, and on a parallel, native medicinal plants are gaining full respect as healing ingredients.

In the best of spas, where loving touch, a calming environment, medicinal plants, and mind–body medicine converge, the therapists see themselves as healers. Highly profession-

In ancient eastern traditions, the lotus flower evokes calmness. (Photo courtesy of Mandara Spa)

al, thoroughly trained men and women, spa therapists are part of a team and eager to make you comfortable with treatments that best suit your needs.

Spa managers understand that healing embraces relationships. Inner health is directly related to intimacy and love. Couples are welcome in the spa for tandem massages and, where possible, for tandem scrubs and wraps.

Privacy is important. Spas have separate areas with separate steam rooms, saunas, and Jacuzzis for men. (One-third to one-half of most spas' clientele is male.) Only the lounge, where everyone wears robes, might be shared by both sexes. In some spas, treatment rooms come with their own steam rooms, lockers, and showers, so you don't have to share space with anyone.

Fitness, exercise, meditation, and healthy foods are natural health builders and stress busters, of course. Many spas offer meditative yoga classes or tai chi, and have nutrition and fitness consultants on board. In many spas, fitness classes and fitness centers with weightlifting machines, free weights, and resistance balls are a short distance away.

The spa experience is about celebrating you, whether you are a man or a woman, twenty-two or ninety-two, pint-sized or plus-sized. You matter. Your health matters. Whoever you are, there is a treatment that suits your taste and temperament. Have fun.

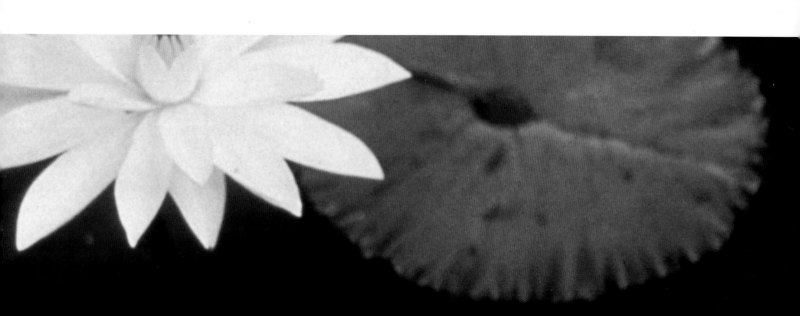

Give yourself plenty of time to relax. (Photo courtesy of Spa Olakino *Salon)

Hydrate before and after your treatment. (Photo by Ray Wong)

Surrender to your healing experience. (Photo courtesy of Mandara Spa)

Spa experience —so refreshing. (Photo courtesy of ANARA Spa)

HOW TO NAVIGATE YOUR WAY THROUGH A SPA

• Long before you are planning to visit the spa, read its menu, and if you aren't sure what certain treatments entail, call to ask for complete descriptions. If you are looking for a specific experience—an outdoor massage, perhaps, or a male or female therapist—by all means express your wishes. Then make your choice—and be kind to yourself; just two or three therapies are plenty for one day.

• Give yourself plenty of time—before, after, and during. Make your appointment several days ahead. On the day of your visit, eat light, wear comfortable clothes, and arrive early enough to fill out a confidential health questionnaire and relax—20 minutes at least. The spa provides you with a robe and slippers, so just slip them on in the locker room and luxuriate. In most spas, swim suits are optional: whatever makes you feel the most comfortable.

• What to do until your appointment? Linger under a hot shower with the spa's soft gels and soaps—if your legs feel stubbly, you may want to shave them so your massage will be extra-smooth. If razors aren't provided, ask. Savor tall glasses of water or iced tea, soak in a whirlpool spa, try the sauna or steam room; these are all excellent ways to prepare your skin for oils and herbs. Wrap yourself in your robe and read a magazine, or meditate in a comfortable chair.

• Forget your cell phone. Celebrate the quiet and privacy of these moments just for you, and respect the quiet and privacy that others seek.

• Your therapist will find you in the relaxation lounge, or in the steam room, or wherever you are. Before the treatment starts, however, make sure that you have removed all your jewelry, and mention any medical concerns or injuries. Many therapies, especially gritty scrubs, work better when you're naked, but if that makes you feel uncomfortable, express your concern and wear your swim suit or ask for disposable underwear. Keep in mind, however, that the staff is discreet and professional. Therapists know exactly how to drape towels and sheets so that you never feel exposed.

• You're on the table, ready to surrender to a sensual, healing experience just for you. Speak up when the touch is too rough or too light, when a wrap is too hot or too tight, when a scrub burns rather than soothes, when questions arise. Otherwise, breathe, let go, and welcome the quiet.

• After, drink a tall glass of water or two to rehydrate. Enjoy the sensation of silky-smooth skin, the lingering scent of aromatherapy oils, the light step of your pampered feet. Perhaps you'll want to leave treatment lotions on, perhaps you want to take a shower again, or wash and style your hair—products are provided in the dressing room—whatever you do, don't rush.

• Relaxed, soft, sensitized, you are vulnerable when you first walk out of the spa. Be gentle. Before you leave the tranquility of the spa, you will, no doubt, want to book another treatment.

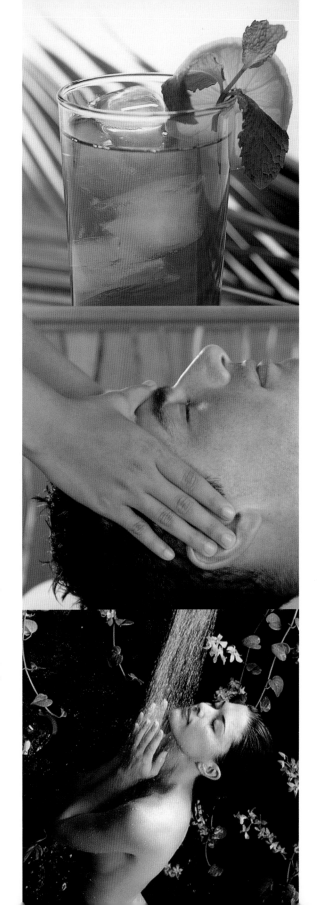

APPENDIX

WHERE TO SPA

O'ahu

Abhasa Waikīkī Spa
The Royal Hawaiian Hotel
2259 Kalākaua Avenue
Honolulu, Hawai'i 96815
808-922-8200
www.abhasa.com

Ihilani Spa
JW Marriott Ihilani Resort and Spa at Ko Olina
92-1001 Olani Street
Kapolei, Hawai'i 96707
808-679-0079
www.ihilani.com

Mandara Spa
Hilton Hawaiian Village Beach Resort & Spa
2005 Kālia Road, Kālia Tower
Honolulu, Hawai'i 96815
808-945-7721
www.mandaraspa.com

Na Ho'ola Spa
Hyatt Regency Waikīkī Resort & Spa
2424 Kalākaua Avenue
Honolulu, Hawai'i 96815
808-921-6097
www.hyattwaikiki.com/Spa/spa.htm

SpaHalekulani
Halekulani
2199 Kālia Road
Honolulu, Hawai'i 96815
808-923-2311
www.halekulani.com

Spa Olakino *Salon
Waikīkī Beach Marriott Resort and Spa
2552 Kalākaua Avenue
Honolulu, Hawai'i 96815
808-922-6611
www.marriottwaikiki.com

Spa Suites
Kāhala Mandarin Oriental, Hawai'i
5000 Kāhala Avenue
Honolulu, Hawai'i 96816
808-739-8938
www.mandarinoriental.com

Maui

Spa Grande
Grand Wailea Resort Hotel & Spa
3850 Wailea Alanui
Wailea, Hawai'i 96753
800-SPA-1933
www.grandwailea.com

Spa Hotel Hāna-Maui
Hotel Hāna-Maui at Hāna Ranch
5031 Hāna Highway
Hāna, Hawai'i 96713
808-248-8211
www.hotelhanamaui.com

Spa Kea Lani
The Fairmont Kea Lani Maui
4100 Wailea Alanui
Wailea, Hawai'i 96753
808-875-2229
www.fairmont.com

Spa Moana
Hyatt Regency Maui Resort & Spa
200 Nohea Kai Drive
Lāhainā, Hawai'i 96761
808-667-4725
www.maui.hyatt.com

The Spa at the Four Seasons Resort Maui
Four Seasons Resort Maui at Wailea
3900 Wailea Alanui
Wailea, Hawai'i 96753
808-874-8000
www.fourseasons.com/maui

Waihua—A Place of Wellness
The Ritz-Carlton, Kapalua
One Ritz-Carlton Drive
Kapalua, Hawai'i 96761
808-669-6200
www.ritzcarlton.com

Hawai'i's Big Island

Hualālai Sports Club & Spa
Four Seasons Resort Hualālai at Historic Ka'ūpūlehu
100 Ka'ūpūlehu Drive
Kona, Hawai'i 96740
808-325-8440
www.fourseasons.com/hualalai

Kohala Sports Club & Spa
Hilton Waikoloa Village
425 Waikoloa Beach Drive
Waikoloa, Hawai'i 96738
808-886-2828
www.kohalaspa.com

Mauna Lani Spa
Mauna Lani Resort
68-1365 Pauoa Road
Kohala Coast, Hawai'i 96743
808-881-7922
www.maunalani.com

Spa Without Walls
The Fairmont Orchid
One North Kanikū Drive
Kohala Coast, Hawai'i 96743
808-887-7540
www.fairmont.com

Kaua'i

ANARA Spa
Hyatt Regency Kaua'i Resort & Spa
1571 Po'ipū Road
Kōloa, Hawai'i 96756
800-742-1234, ext. 4949
www.anaraspa.com

Lāna'i

The Spa at Mānele Bay Hotel
Mānele Bay Hotel
Lāna'i City, Lāna'i, Hawai'i 96763
808-565-2088
www.islandoflanai.com

ADDITIONAL SPAS

Almost any resort in the Hawaiian Islands has spa
services in one form or another. The facilities that
you see there do not have to be state-of-the-art
for you to experience top-notch treatments.

O'ahu

Aveda Lifestyle Salon & Spa
Ala Moana Shopping Center
1450 Ala Moana Boulevard, 3rd Floor
Honolulu, Hawai'i 96814
808-947-6141
www.aveda.com

Paul Brown Salon & Spa
1200 Ala Moana Boulevard
Honolulu, Hawai'i 96814
808-591-1881
www.paulbrownhawaii.com

Hawaiian Rainforest Salon & Spa
Pacific Beach Hotel
2490 Kalākaua Avenue
Honolulu, Hawai'i 96815
808-922-1233
www.pacificbeachhotel.com

Heaven on Earth Salon & Day Spa
1050 Alakea Street
Honolulu, Hawai'i 96813
808-599-5501
www.heavenonearthhawaii.com

Serenity Spa Hawai'i
Outrigger Reef on the Beach
2169 Kālia Road
Honolulu, Hawai'i 96815
808-926-2882
www.serenityhawaii.com

Spa Luana
Turtle Bay Resort
57-091 Kamehameha Highway
Kahuku, Hawai'i 96731
808-293-6000
www.turtlebayresort.com

Touch 'N Go Massage
Renaissance Ilikai Hotel Fitness Center
1777 Ala Moana Boulevard
Honolulu, Hawai'i 96815
808-941-8414

Maui

Luana Spa Retreat
5050 Uakea Road
Hana, Hawai'i 96713
808-248-8855
www.luanaspa.com

Mandara Spa
Wailea Marriott
3700 Wailea Alanui
Wailea, Hawai'i 96753
808-879-1922
www.waileamarriott.com

Kapalua Bay Hotel Salon & Massage Center
Kapalua Bay Hotel
One Bay Drive
Kapalua, Hawai'i 96761
808-669-5656
www.kapaluabayhotel.com

The Spa at the Westin Maui
The Westin Maui
2365 Ka'anapali Parkway
Lāhainā, Hawai'i 96761
808-667-2525
www.westinmaui.com

Hawai'i's Big Island

Paul Brown Salon & Spa
Hāpuna Beach Prince Hotel
62-100 Kauna'oa Drive
Kamuela, Hawai'i 96743
808-880-3335
www.princeresortshawaii.com

Hawaiian Rainforest Salon & Spa
Waikoloa Beach Marriott
69-275 Waikoloa Beach Drive
Waikoloa, Hawai'i 96738
808-886-6789
www.waikoloabeachmarriott.com

Kalona Salon & Spa
'Ohana Keauhou Beach Resort
78-6740 Ali'i Drive
Kailua-Kona, Hawai'i 96740
808-322-9373
www.kalonaspa.com

Kaua'i

Hart-Felt Massage & Day Spa
Waimea Plantation Cottages
9400 Kaumualii Highway
Kekaha, Hawai'i 96752
808-338-2240
www.hartfeltmassage.com

Princeville Health Club & Spa
Princeville Resort
53900 Kūhiō Highway
Princeville, Hawai'i 96722
808-826-5030
www.princeville.com

RESOURCES

ISLAND SPA PRODUCTS

Warren Botanicals
888-848-0642
www.warrenbotanicals.com
This Big Island-based company creates treatments with medicinal-grade oils as well as spa products that use plant infusions and essential oils. Their popular Relief Line was originally designed for professional athletes and has become an essential part of the traveler's survival kit. It contains four vials of oils: Muscle and Joint Relief, Stress Relief, Respiratory Relief, and Migraine Relief.

Island Essence
888-878-3800
www.islandessence.com
From upcountry Kula on Maui comes a full line of pure and natural home spa products that include massage oils, bath oils, scrubs, mineral salts, and lotions. Fragrances include pīkake, passion fruit, coconut-mango, and white ginger. Island Essence also develops spa formulas for several island spas.

Hawaiian Girl Botanicals
808-335-0758
www.hawaiiangirl.net
Created by experienced massage therapists on the Island of Kaua'i, these all-natural oils, mists, lotions, and bath salts each are offered with a choice of five aromatherapy blends, including sweet citrus, forest scents, and floral jasmine formulas.

Maui Kula Lavender
808-878-3004
www.mauikulalavender.com

Maui Lavender
808-250-2284
www.mauilavender.com
These two pioneer companies have expanding lavender fields on the slopes of Haleakalā. Subtly scented, handcrafted products and information about lavender's healing properties can be found on-line. Visitors to the island can also book lavender tours.

Monoi Tiare Tahiti
Tahiti's legendary pure coconut oil, scented with a variety of tropical flowers, can be ordered at www.monoi.com. In addition, the Web site sells coconut oils scented with sandalwood, ylang ylang, and jasmine. The company also offers coconut oil-based soaps with these exotic scents.

Island Herbal
808-882-7004
www.thehawaiianspa.com
Island Herbal is a small company just outside upcountry Waimea on the Big Island, established in 1990, that sells a vast array of natural spa products, including pure plant oils such as *kukui* nut oil. Here you can also find natural baby skin care products from the islands, soothing eye pillows, CDs, and gift baskets.

ISLAND RELAXATION MUSIC

Hawaiian Healing Journey
Relax with island music that follows the soaring, dancing, and gentle flight of the *'i'iwi* bird, Hawai'i's beloved, rare honeycreeper, through a landscape of hidden valleys, across volcanic slopes and down to gentle ocean shores. Steve Jones and Bryan Kessler have created their hour-long CD specifically for meditation and massage. Natural sounds are enhanced by keyboard, chant, guitar, and nose flute.

Island Treasures

Traditional, nostalgic island melodies find a soothing translation in these gentle jazz arrangements created by Kohala, a trio of classic and acoustic guitarists. Without any vocals or distractions, the twelve songs provide romantic background music. Kohala's first CD, "Kohala," interprets contemporary island melodies in similar meditative ways.

ISLAND FLAVORS

Numerous companies—especially coffee estates and gifts shops—sell hand-selected island teas on their Web sites.

The teas from Pu'u'ala Farm and Ranch on the slopes of Mauna Kea are organic and include kava and *noni* tea, as well as sweeter flavors. Web: www.puuala.com. Another well-established tea packer is Traditional Hawaiian Herbal Teas: www.hawaiianherbalteas.com.

Currently, about six hundred farms, small and large, produce authentic Kona coffee, and the options for buying on the Internet are expanding almost daily. Many Kona coffee growers are choosing to go organic. An excellent place to start for a rich, certified organic Kona coffee to use in scrubs—and in cups—is Rooster Farms, one of the oldest organic coffee estates, located just south of Kealakekua: www.roosterfarms.com.

Hawaiian Commercial and Sugar Company in Pu'unēnē on Maui, one of two remaining sugar operations in the Islands—the other one is on Kaua'i—sells pure Maui turbinado sugar on a Web site dedicated to natural cane sugars at www.mauibrand.com.

SPA SPEAK

GLOSSARY OF SPA TERMINOLOGY

Aromatherapy – The ancient healing art of using essential oils of plants, leaves, bark, roots, seeds, resin, and flowers for their therapeutic properties to treat physical and emotional issues. There is scientific proof that just eight aromatic molecules can activate a person's sense of smell. Olfactory receptors inside the nose are directly linked to the limbic system in the brain, which is the seat of emotions, memories, intuition, and sexual response. That is why scents can have such a powerful influence on thoughts, emotions, desires, and moods.

Ayurveda – A healing tradition with roots in ancient India that employs a large variety of techniques to restore balance, including nutrition, herbs, aromatherapy, massage, and meditation.

Chakra – Refers to the seven energy centers of the body. Taken from the Sanskrit word meaning "wheel." The seven *chakras* are the root of the trunk of the body, the genitals, the stomach, the heart, the throat, the forehead (third eye), and the top of the head.

Color Therapy – Dates back to ancient Egypt and is based on the law of attraction, where the vibration of the color attracts a similar vibration in the human body. Spas use colors in the decoration of the treatment rooms, in the salts and oils added to baths, and to hydrotherapy baths that beam colored light into the bath.

Day Spa – A spa offering a variety of spa services to clients on a day-use basis without accommodations.

Destination Spa – A spa whose purpose is to provide guests with lifestyle improvement and health enhancement through a program of spa services, physical fitness, spa cuisine, educational programs, and on-site accommodations.

Essential Oils – Aromatic liquid substances, which are extracted from plants, leaves, bark, roots, seeds, resin, and flowers and are used in the medicinal, food, and cosmetic industries.

Exfoliation – Skin treatment where the outer layer of dead skin cells is sloughed off. A variety of techniques can be used and the treatment is called accordingly: loofah rub, salt scrub, body scrub, and body glow.

Herbal Wrap – A therapeutic spa treatment that uses warm linen or cotton sheets that have been steeped like tea bags in aromatic herbs. The body is wrapped in the herb-soaked sheets and then covered with blankets or towels to prevent the moist heat from escaping. Herbal wraps help relax the muscles, soothe soreness, and soften skin.

Hydrotherapy – The generic term for water therapies using jets, underwater massage, and mineral baths. It also can mean a whirlpool bath, hot Roman pool, hot tub, Jacuzzi, cold plunge, or mineral bath.

Lomilomi – The Hawaiian word for massage. *Lomilomi* is a rhythmical healing ritual that begins and may end with a *pule* (prayer) and usually incorporates long, flowing strokes using the forearm and elbow, rather than just the hands.

Loofah – A dried natural plant, like a dried sponge, used to slough off dry, dead skin.

Reflexology – Ancient Chinese technique using pressure point massage (usually on the feet, but also hands and ears) to restore the flow of energy throughout the body. Charts show which zones in the feet, hands, and ears correspond to specific internal organs.

Resort/Hotel Spa – A spa within a resort or hotel providing spa services, fitness, and wellness components. Many also offer spa cuisine menu choices.

Salt Glow – A body scrub consisting of coarse sea salt usually mixed with essential oils and water that cleanses pores and removes dead skin. A gentle shower and application of a body moisturizer follow.

Sauna – A dry heat treatment (at less than 10 percent humidity) in a wood-lined room with temperatures of 160 to 210 degrees Fahrenheit, designed to bring about sweating to cleanse the body of impurities. After a sauna, a cool shower closes the pores and brings down body temperature.

Seaweed (Limu) Wrap – A mask made primarily of powdered seaweed and water that is painted over the body, which is then wrapped to absorb the minerals, rare trace elements, vitamins, and proteins that soak into the blood stream, revitalizing the entire body.

Shiatsu – Means finger *(shi)* pressure *(atsu)*. This massage is a cross between acupressure and massage and was developed in Japan in the 1940s. Like acupressure, Shiatsu works with the body's vital points and energy meridians or channels and uses finger-thumb-palm pressure to stimulate these points and encourage energy flow through the energy meridians.

Shirodhara – Ayurvedic treatment in which a stream of warm sesame oil is poured onto the "third eye," the point on the forehead between the eyes that is said to be the access point to spiritual wisdom.

Spa Cuisine – Fresh, natural foods low in saturated fats and cholesterol, with an emphasis on fresh fruit, fish, and vegetables, whole grains, low-fat dairy products, lean proteins, and an avoidance of added salt and products containing artificial colorings, flavorings, and preservatives.

Swedish Massage – The most commonly offered and best-known type of massage. Devised at the University of Stockholm in 1812 by Henri Peter Ling, this technique employs five different movements (long strokes; kneading of individual muscles; percussive, tapping movement; rolling of the fingers; and vibration) and oils beneficial to the skin. Used to improve circulation, ease muscle aches and tension, improve flexibility, and create relaxation.

Swiss Shower – A multi-headed, stand-up shower that sprays you with water from three sides, providing a full-body water massage that increases circulation and reduces muscle tension.

Tai Chi – An ancient Chinese martial art form of meditation in movement, which combines mental concentration, coordinated breathing, and a series of slow, graceful body movements. While this may look like a slow-motion dance, it is used for relaxation, centering, and self-defense.

Termé – Latin word, which means, "of, relating to, using, producing, or caused by heat." At spas, terme is associated with heated water treatments.

Thalassotherapy – An ancient Greek therapy (thalasso is Greek for "sea") that uses the therapeutic benefits of seawater and seaweed, which are rich in vitamins, minerals, and trace elements. Treatments include seaweed body wraps, individual baths of fresh seawater equipped with powerful underwater jets for deep massage, and soaking in pools with seawater warmed to body temperature.

Vichy Shower – A relaxing rinse with multiple horizontal showerheads that provide a gentle head-to-toe rain shower as you lie on the treatment table. The Vichy is often used with body scrubs and wraps in lieu of a conventional shower that requires you to leave the treatment table.

Watsu – A massage treatment performed in a private pool that combines shiatsu massage, Indian *chakra* work, and yoga. Shiatsu practitioner Harold Dull developed the technique after discovering the effects of massage could be enhanced in warm water. Watsu sessions take place in warm, waist-deep water, with the client and therapist wearing swimsuits.

Yoga – Derived from the Sanskrit word for "union," this ancient Indian system of stretching and toning the body through *asanas* (poses) and *pranayama* (breathing techniques) integrates the body and mind. Yoga was originally created to prepare the body for meditation. Its health benefits include increased flexibility, relaxation, and improved posture and muscle tone.

About the Authors

 **SHERRIE STRAUSFOGEL** writes about spas, beauty, health, cuisine, and travel. Her work has appeared in more than 100 magazines, newspapers, guidebooks, and Web sites. Based in Honolulu, she has spoken at spa and wellness conferences from Miami to Maui, traveled to more than 50 countries, and visited many of the leading spas in the U.S., Canada, Mexico, Europe and Asia.

 **SOPHIA V. SCHWEITZER,** an award-winning freelance writer and author, lives in North Kohala on The Big Island. A co-author of numerous books, she has contributed to dozens of national publications. Her book Kohala 'A-ina, A History of North Kohala became the recipient of a Kahili and the Best-of-Show in the annual statewide Keep-It-Hawaii awards in 2004. She specializes in Hawai'i-related topics, healing and wellness, complementary medicine, and sustainable living.